D1224563

PREMIER PROFILES IN SCIENCE SERIES

Already Published

SIGMUND FREUD

ROBERT OPPENHEIMER

IVAN PAVLOV

Forthcoming Titles

ALBERT EINSTEIN

LOUIS PASTEUR

FREDERIC JOLIOT-CURIE

IVAN PAVLOV

The Man and His Theories

by Hilaire Cuny

TRANSLATED BY PATRICK EVANS

A FAWCETT PREMIER BOOK
FAWCETT PUBLICATIONS, INC., GREENWICH, CONN.
MEMBER OF AMERICAN BOOK PUBLISHERS COUNCIL, INC.

First British edition published 1964 by Souvenir Press Ltd.

First American edition published 1965 by Paul S. Eriksson, Inc., New York.

This book contains the complete text of the original hardcover edition.

Library of Congress Catalog Card Number: 65-15778

First Fawcett Premier printing, June 1966

Published by Fawcett World Library, 67 West 44th Street, New York, N. Y. 10036. Printed in the United States of America.

In homage to Dr Paul Chauchard, who demonstrated the psycho-physiological integrity of the human being, and who is working toward a synthesis of the idealistic and materialistic points of view

Contents

SELECTED WRITINGS

With the exception of (*d*) and parts of (*f*), all these excerpts are taken from I. P. Pavlov, *Selected Works* (English edition. Moscow: Foreign Languages Publishing House, 1955).

IVAN PAVLOV

1

The Thinker and Experimenter *

EVER since man started thinking, since he became capable of communicating his experience in speech and subsequently in writing, which is an extension of speech, thousands of millions of individuals have made their minute contributions and enabled our species to "progress" in the widely varied fields of the arts, sciences and technology. But a few of these individuals have specially distinguished themselves by contributing gigantic quanta to the universal task—in some cases completely upsetting their predecessors' theories, bringing light amid darkness, and imposing their names on posterity.

One such individual is undeniably Ivan Petrovich Pavlov; with whose works, however, not many present-day readers have had the chance of becoming familiar. If there are some in whose minds the words "conditioned reflex"† arouse more or less distant memories of something they once learned about the mechanism of glandular secretions, there

* At the end of the book will be found a Glossary of such technical terms as might be an obstacle to the layman.

† Except in quotations, we shall always use the term "conditioned reflexes" in preference to "conditional reflexes." Pavlov himself, at the end of his investigations, admitted that the former was "more correct."

are very few who have felt the urge, or have been encouraged by their teachers, to draw any connection between this elementary process and the very close relationship which it bears to the reactions, both physiological and psychological, of the human being as a whole.

The public at large knows almost nothing about Pavlov, because no book written in layman's terms has been put before it. When the famous physiologist died, in 1936, the only works one could consult about him were a few papers composed for specialists; some of these papers were merely duplicated, not printed; others lay scattered and hidden in medical or philosophical journals. It is true that since then a large number of doctors, biologists, physiologists, psychologists and philosophers, each writing from the point of view of his own domain, have commented copiously on Pavlov's work and in some cases criticized it, but always in a particular and fragmentary way or else in such a context as rarely crosses the horizon of the average reader. That is why in the present book we shall not rest content with describing Pavlov the man and reporting the main facts of his life, but shall also try to present, explain and comment upon his researches and their implications.

Before we get into the thick of things, it seems imperative to show briefly in what sense Pavlov's thinking revolutionized conventionally accepted ideas, and how it was that observations on salivary and gastric secretions led him to demonstrate with precision the close interdependence of psychical activities and physiological reactions—an achievement destined to have an enormous influence on the study of human and animal behavior, on neuropathology and indeed on medicine in general, on the study of memory, sleep and hypnosis, and also on cybernetics, which, as if by feedback (to use a term from cybernetics itself), has contributed so much to our investigations of the nervous system.

Pavlov has done more than anyone else to destroy the Cartesian myth of body and soul as separate entities. No one has so effectively illuminated the reciprocal connections between physiochemical, biological and physiological reactions on the one hand, and psychic (or supposedly psychic) reactions on the other. Though he often refused to assume the psychologist's role, it was not because he rejected psychology as a valid philosophical study of vital manifestations; he was simply reacting against the subjectivism of the psychologists of his day. As we are reminded by M. François Le Ny, to whom we are indebted for a recent (and remarkable) study of the nature and implications of conditioning, "one finds here and there a testimony to his esteem for objective psychology."

It was through the establishment of permanent fistulas in dogs, and above all through the difficult surgical feat of isolating what was termed "the miniature stomach"—neither of which procedures in any way upsets the dog's vital processes, once it has recovered from the shock of the operation—that Pavlov, showing a skill in surgery to match his originality in research, succeeded in laying the foundations of this objective psychology which drew its data from life itself—that is to say, from physiology—and was no longer the vassal of arbitrary metaphysical views tinged with anthropomorphism.

For mental life is not a "thing in itself," any more than physiological or physiochemical phenomena are "things in themselves." Mental life, as every serious scientific man is now willing to admit, is not "merely" an epiphenomenon of biological life, any more than life itself is "merely" an epiphenomenon of physiochemistry; but it remains true of both of them that they cannot manifest themselves externally without a material substratum developing dynamically in time and space. Reservations about our ignorance of the deeper causes underlying the primordial movements of matter cannot prevent us from adopting any other definition of biological and psychological phenomena than that given by scientific materialism: life is a form of the movement of matter, or, if you prefer, a form of material evolution, and mental life is a quality externalized either in individual complexes (i.e. people) or in a group of individuals (i.e. a society); and this externalization takes place more effectively in proportion as the biological structure of the species concerned has reached a more complex stage of development (emergence of a nervous system more fully adapted, more specialized, for receiving messages and registering them in memory, and for envisaging a wider gamut of possible reactions from which to choose)—a state of affairs which allows contact between the three environments to be closer, more detailed and more delicate and to include the individual's awareness of existing as an independent part of the cosmic whole in space and time.

Obviously such an explanation is by no means the last

word, but it does represent the facts as we know them: for we see clearly that the universe is subject to the laws of energy and matter, and that the existence of the phenomena surrounding us, or the succession of cosmic events, does not depend on transcendent factors lying outside those laws and capable of transgressing them. Causality ("no effect without a cause") is the only standard of judgment on which we can rely. Now the fundamental fact within our field of observation is that energy—of which we know strictly nothing, except that it "is"—can be transformed into mass, and conversely. We also observe that, in ways proceeding from the principal effects of force (gravitational, nuclear, electromagnetic), all the structures we are capable of perceiving with our senses, or with instruments which extend the power of our senses, are born, change and die. Pushing our observation further, we see these structures continually acting on one another in accordance with these same effects of force, which govern biological complexes as they do all others; biological complexes, as Dr. Laborit has lately shown in a brilliant exposition, are self-regulating systems, dependent, both internally and in their relations with the external environment, on the principles of cybernetics, which makes use of just those force-effects we have mentioned.

In what way does the psychical effect (or mental life) differ from force-effects? Just in this, that it has long appeared to escape the fate of being determined by them. But is it inherently capable of so escaping; and, if it is, in what degree? In the present state of our knowledge we can give no answer, positive or negative. Of course it seems to us that, in creatures with a highly developed nervous system, mental life involves a certain "freedom of choice"—which, however tiny it may be in the case of the individual as a separate entity, could be collectively harnessed so as to offer the species in question enormous scope for its own evolution. Naturally, we are here thinking especially of the human race; however, this may be just "anthropomorphic" conceit.

Pavlov's researches made it possible to understand that by far the greater part of the behavior of living creatures depended on reflex mechanisms describable in physiological terms, and that the various manifestations of higher nervous activity were the result, as his spiritual master Sechenov had already put it, "of the relations continuously obtaining between the organism and its surrounding milieu, at the same time as they were the result of the conditions determining the organism's existence."

Neither Sechenov nor Pavlov was the first to have seen the importance of reflex activity. It had been clearly perceived by Descartes, a bust of whom occupied a place of honor in Pavlov's laboratory, but almost nobody except Charles Richet had thought of establishing a correlation between the very anciently observed fact of salivation appearing without any direct alimentary influence being brought to bear on the mucous membrane of the mouth, and organic reflex processes.

The Greek naturalists had noted that the mere sight and fragrance of attractive food, and even the thought of eating a good meal, were capable of producing abundant salivation —an effect to which popular language bears witness with such expressions as "his mouth watered." Charles Richet had put forward the idea that the cause was "psychic reflexes," whose point of departure was "traces of previous excitations, inscribed at the cerebral level."

It was while carrying out classical researches on digestion that Pavlov was led to convert this idea into exact observation.

EARLY HARDSHIPS

Ivan Petrovich Pavlov was born on September 14, 1849, in the ancient Russian town of Ryazan. His father, Piotr Dmitrievich Pavlov, was a priest. Ivan Petrovich was the eldest of eleven children, and from an early age had to discharge the responsibilities of this position by helping his father in the garden and relieving his mother of certain domestic burdens. Throughout his life he retained a deep respect for manual work; his famous letter to the Donetz miners includes the following passage: "All my life I have loved and still love work, mental and physical, and the latter perhaps even more than the former. And I experienced the greatest satisfaction every time I succeeded in transplanting a good idea into my physical work—that is, when I was able to combine brain and hand."

Headstrong and turbulent, like all children, he had fallen from a balustrade at the age of seven and sustained a severe blow to his skull on the tiled floor below. The shock to his system was such that he was unable to attend school until he was eleven; any prolonged mental effort was too much for him. But his education was not neglected in consequence, for his father, without being learned, had had a good education himself and gave him the benefit of his knowledge. While gardening, he taught the boy some of the elements of botany, and when the spade cut an earthworm into two wriggling pieces which subsequently became complete worms, Ivan received his first lesson on the mechanism of nervous activity.

In 1860 he passed directly into the town's theological seminary. Of course, religious instruction had its place in the program, but many of the staff were professing liberals. "We had a number of excellent teachers," records Pavlov's brief *Autobiography*. One of them in particular, the priest Feofilakt Orlov, "was a man of lofty ideals. In general, in the seminary at that time (I do not know how it was afterward) one could follow one's own intellectual inclinations, which was not the case, regrettably so, in the notorious Tolstoy gymnasiums * (and, I think, also in the present ones). One could lag in a given subject and get on in another, but this did not threaten one with trouble, including expulsion; in point of fact it focused attention on one, and gave rise to speculation about the talents and abilities of the student in question."

We cannot doubt that there was plenty of such speculation in the case of Ivan Petrovich, whose end-of-term reports were by no means liberally adorned with good final percentages.

Pavlov's character was ardent and generous. In spite of belonging to the orthodox hierarchy, his father had the reputation of holding "advanced ideas," and he brought up his sons to love justice and respect human dignity. He spoke out vehemently against the powerful and defended the unfortunate. Ivan Petrovich's inclinations received all possible encouragement at his father's hands.

The boy's first years of schooling coincided with the widespread flowering of a progressive movement. With passionate interest, he read Bielinsky, Herzen, Chernishevsky and above all Pisarev, the man responsible for introducing the analytical method into Russian criticism:

"Influenced by the literature of the 'sixties, and particularly

* "Named after D. Tolstoy, Czarist Minister of Public Education, who converted the gymnasiums into scholastic schools with barrack-like discipline.—*Ed.*" (Pavlov, *Selected Works,* p.43.)

by Pisarev, our intellectual interests turned to natural science, and many, myself included, decided to take this subject at the University.

". . . I entered the Petersburg University and studied in the natural history section of the physics and mathematics faculty."

This was in 1870. No more than vague echoes of the Franco-Prussian War had entered Russia, which was shaken by internal stirrings at the time. Pavlov was just twenty-one. He was filled with faith in science and burning to acquire new knowledge which would be profitable to himself, and which he hoped to pass on to others.

"The faculty was in its heyday at the time. We had a number of professors with great names in science, men who were outstanding as lecturers. I chose animal physiology for my major course and took chemistry as a minor. We physiologists were tremendously impressed by Cyon.* We were fascinated by his ingeniously simple exposition of the most complex physiological questions and his skill in conducting experiments. One can never forget such a teacher. I did my first physiological work under his tutelage."

It was doubtless this first work which decided the course of his astounding career. The subject under investigation was the entire apparatus of the pancreatic nerves, and Pavlov carried out this study so conscientiously that he won a gold medal.

By 1875 Pavlov had finished his studies and obtained the degree of Candidate of Natural Sciences, which entitled him to work for a medical qualification. In his *Autobiography* he says that this was "not for the purpose of becoming a physician, but with the idea that after getting the degree of doctor of medicine I would qualify for a chair in physiology. I must say, however, that at the time this plan seemed a vain dream because a professorship appeared as something unattainable, incredible."

When he entered the Academy of Medicine he was to become assistant to Professor Cyon, replacing Chernov, who had gone abroad to study. But an incredible thing happened: despite his great ability and knowledge, Cyon was summarily

* The brothers Cyon had discovered the existence of an accelerator nerve in the heart.

dismissed. It was a period of brilliant men, but also of arbitrary authority.

Out of loyalty, Pavlov left the Academy of Medicine and entered the Veterinary Institute as assistant to Professor Ustimovich. When, in 1878, Ustimovich gave up his chair, Pavlov became a collaborator of Botkin, who was a pupil of Claude Bernard.

Pavlov was to work for ten years on end in the laboratory of Professor Botkin's clinic. A wretched laboratory it was; a dilapidated shed, which had been used first as a porter's lodge and then as a drying room. But Botkin could offer only what he had, and he had fitted the place up as best he could with the scanty means available to him. Science was not in favor with the feudal and military caste which ruled Russia for the Czar. The experimental equipment was rudimentary and the salaries of the research workers were glaringly inadequate.

To avoid the expense of taking a room in town, Pavlov slept on a palliasse in the "laboratory," which he continued to do even after his marriage in 1881; his wife, Serafina Vassilievna Kartatievskaya, had to lodge with her brother-in-law, Dmitri Petrovich Pavlov, assistant to the famous chemist Mendeleyev.

However, Botkin was in no way responsible for his assistant's poverty, and Pavlov remained ever afterward full of praise for him: "He personified in the highest degree the legitimate and fruitful union of medicine and physiology, the two disciplines which under our very eyes are building our knowledge of the organism and which are the foundation of our constant endeavor to improve living conditions and maintain health."

Under Botkin, Pavlov enjoyed complete independence: "I had no obligations in regard to the clinic. Although I collaborated in group undertakings, I was able to devote myself to all sorts of inquiries of my own. And in any case I had nothing to lose by cooperating with others; on the contrary, I acquired new knowledge in this collaboration. From our discussions I gained the habit of 'physiological reasoning.' Gradually, I progressed until no laboratory technique held any secrets for me. Then I was able to prepare my thesis on the centrifugal nerves of the heart, and begin my researches on digestion."

In 1883, the year when he presented this doctoral thesis,

his wife gave birth to their first child. Serafina Vassilievna had already suffered a miscarriage, caused says one of Pavlov's biographers, Professor Asratian, "by bad living conditions." The outlook for the survival of the child, Mirtnik, was unpromising. The doctor prescribed a stay in the country for mother and baby. The problem of finding the necessary money for fares and lodging was acute. It was out of the question to rent an apartment or a villa in the country round St. Petersburg: "So we had to resign ourselves," writes Serafina Vassilievna, "to accepting the hospitality of a sister-in-law who lived in a remote village, far in the south."

But where was the money for the long railway journey to come from? "Only with difficulty," Serafina Vassilievna's memoirs go on to say, "did Ivan and Dmitri scrape up enough for a ticket as far as Ryazan. They gave me a letter in which they begged their father to raise a loan so that the child and I could reach our destination."

But, alas, despite all these sacrifices, little Mirtnik remained frail and sickly. His illness took a fatal turn; he wasted away and died in the distant region which had been so hard to reach.

Pavlov was deeply afflicted, but his thesis was absorbing all his attention. He passed brilliantly, winning another gold medal, the title of doctor and the rank of professor, together with a scholarship which he spent on a visit to Germany. He was away for two years (1884-6), and took advantage of his travels to frequent assiduously the laboratory of Rudolf Heidenhain in Breslau, and that of Karl Ludwig in Leipzig.

STUDIES ON GASTRIC SECRETIONS

In 1877 Pavlov had published his first work, entitled *Experimental Data Concerning the Accommodating Mechanism of the Blood Vessels*. In it the reflex regulation of the blood circulation was presented in an original way. His doctoral thesis had been concerned with the centrifugal nerves of the heart. On his return from Germany he focused his attention on the study of glandular secretions—saliva and gastric juices.

Long ago, in 1822, the Canadian Dr. Beaumont had had the chance of observing *in vivo* the accidentally exposed stomach of a trapper who had been wounded in the abdomen by a gunshot at point-blank range; he had seen that the arrival of food in the stomach "automatically" occasioned the production of "humors," by which the food was decomposed; and, following these observations, it had been generally understood that the mechanism of digestion depended on the agency of complex chemical products which were termed "juices."

Claude Bernard had shown that the gastric juice transformed nutritional matter into compounds assimilable by the organism, and that only after this transformation had taken place could nutriment be distributed throughout the economy of the organism, or else passed on to other organs, such as the liver, for further transformation or for storage. Pavlov's original ambition was simply to render this knowledge more detailed and complete, although his attention, like that of other specialists, had already been attracted by the phenomena of the so-called "psychic secretions," which he intended to study alongside the physical ones. He selected the dog as his experimental animal, and devised surgical techniques which made it possible to establish "permanent fistulas" in connection with the principal organs of digestion (salivary glands, stomach, liver, pancreas, parts of the intestine).

These techniques are now classical. In the case of the salivary glands, an opening is made along Warton's canal (in the case of the submaxillary gland) or the canal of Steno (in the case of the parotid gland), and, a cutaneous incision having been made along the median line of the floor of the mouth, the mucosa containing the orifice of the canal is sewn to the edges of the incision (the canal having first been brought through the suprahyoid muscles in the case of the submaxillary gland, or the masseter and buccinator muscles in that of the parotid). When the wound has cicatrized sufficiently, a glass funnel is attached to the fistula by means of a special cement, so that drops can be counted; the saliva is also collected in a graduated test tube (quantative measurement of secretion) and is subsequently analyzed (qualitative observation).

Pavlov perceived at once that, whatever the circumstances in which the secretion had been caused—that is, whether by actual contact between food and the oral mucosa, or only by the sight of food—the saliva produced was qualitatively identical for a given kind of food. Was this true of gastric secretion also?

Observation in this case was far more difficult. Gastric fistulas had already been successfully made, notably by Bassov in Russia and Blondot at Nancy, in France. But the gastric fluid obtained was mixed with food, and exact qualitative analysis could not be made. In Germany, in Ludwig's laboratory and later in Heidenhain's, Pavlov had witnessed various attempts to obtain uncontaminated specimens of gastric juice, fit for analysis, but the results had not been wholly satisfactory. He resolved to make an entirely new attack on the problem: part of the stomach must be isolated, so that food could not reach it; at the same time that part would retain the vasculation and innervation normal to the rest of the organ and would thus represent, in Pavlov's own expression, "a mirror of what goes on in the stomach as a whole."

This is the operation of the "isolated stomach," the technique of the "miniature stomach"—a portion of the stomach which is shut off from the rest and can be provided, by means of a fistula, with a drop counter and a test tube attached externally, on the animal's flank. The operation is carried out as follows: An incision shaped like a hairpin is made in the wall of the stomach, in the pyloric region, and the edges of the wound thus formed are joined by suture; the same is done with those of the flap of tissue which is to form the miniature stomach. At the point of junction between the two (that is, between the artificially created pouch and the stomach proper) the mucosa is severed and stitched to itself on one side and the other, so that each part has its own complete and independent mucous lining. The pouch is thus isolated and constitutes a miniature stomach.

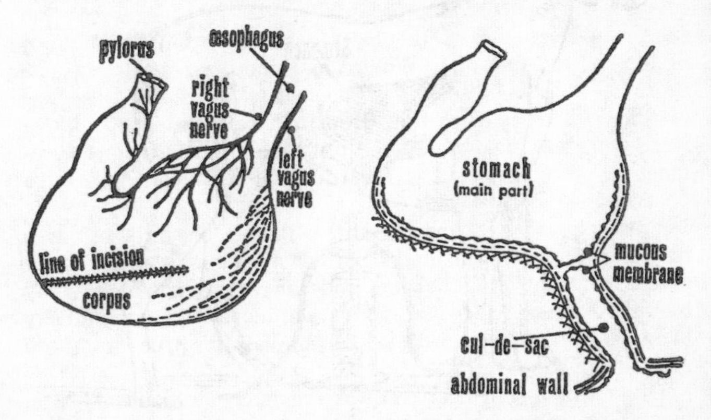

Such an experiment was extremely difficult to carry out while keeping the dog not only alive but in perfect health. Even to make the attempt required considerable daring. In a speech delivered on the seventy-fifth birthday of his former teacher, Professor Samoïlov did not disguise the uneasiness he had felt during the early trials: "At first the operation was not a success. Thirty dogs were sacrificed in vain. Much time—almost six months—and much effort, were expended; the faint-hearted were for giving the whole thing up. I remember that several professors of subjects related to physiology declared the attempt was bound to fail because the location of the blood vessels in the stomach rendered it impossible. Ivan Petrovich laughed, as only he could, at these assertions. A few more efforts and success was on the way."

Let us reply to criticism in advance by saying: Yes, Pavlov did sacrifice a large number of animals, just as they are still sacrificed every day in laboratories the world over. I am very far from believing that we should be justified in making merely scornful answers to the protests of animal lovers. Although experiments on animals are carried out with anesthetics and with every necessary antiseptic precaution, there is no doubt

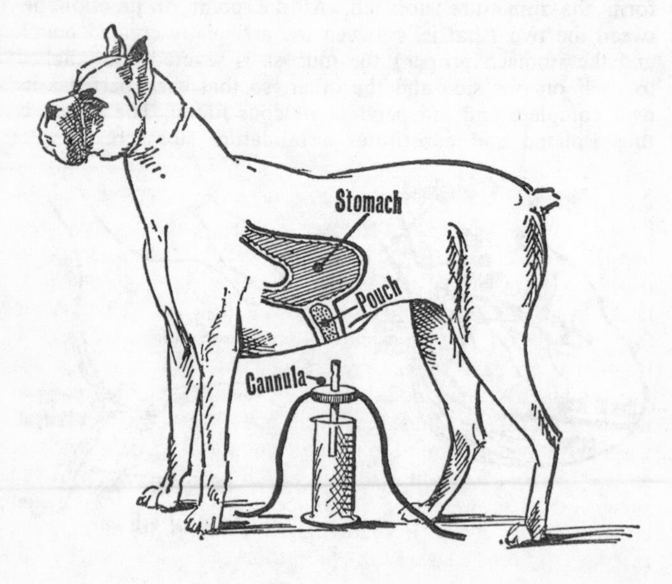

at all that experimental animals do suffer, even if only during the post-operational period, and after that by their loss of liberty, and by the emotional disturbance, however slight, to which they are subjected by the presence of the recording instruments required in obtaining clinical results. It is always with a certain feeling of distress that I watch operations on animals (though the subjects, I repeat, are carefully anesthetized, since from the scientific point of view alone we are bound to remember that misleading results would be gained from an organism in a traumatic state and struggling with all its might to escape from that state). I have, perhaps, been more deeply moved while watching an operation on a dog whose heart had been arrested and opened, in some clinic in Paris, than I was at Budapest when I followed from beginning to end the removal of an enormous malignant tumor from the stomach of an emaciated sixty-year-old human patient, whose heart I could see beating meanwhile, and whose lungs were filling and emptying. For until the operation the dog had been healthy and happy, "glad to be alive," whereas the human wreck laid out on the operating table, under the harsh lights of the theater, was dying. The human sufferer was gaining from the operation; the dog could only lose. This undoubtedly poses a problem of ethics—namely, whether the form of life known as *man* makes the best of his knowledge, and, in consequence, has any right to make use of other forms of life for his own advantage.

But men we are, and it is as men that we must think and reason: "Sensitive souls" we may be, but we are bound to reflect that in order to preserve our species we are *forced* to destroy life, and that the same law holds good throughout the organic world. With few exceptions, we are omnivorous and therefore carnivorous; the human frame requires animal proteins for its nourishment. Directly or indirectly, and whether they will or no, even the most ascetic vegetarians consume living matter. And when they are ill they profit from the advances which science could never have made without experiments on animals, and they will continue to profit, often without knowing it or perhaps without wanting to know, just as the rest of us profit and will continue to profit from the slaughter of the bleating lamb, or the cow or pig, which are treated far worse in slaughterhouses than are dogs, cats, rabbits, frogs and newts in the laboratory.

The great diminution in infantile mortality is due to medicine and surgery, whose progress, in turn, is undoubtedly due to experiments on animals.* If there are fewer lunatics, or at least if mental patients suffer less than they used to, this again is an advance which we owe to the study of the higher nervous system *in vivo*, the subjects of such study being in most cases animals. No biologist or physiologist in our day "tortures" animals; all do whatever they can (and would do so even if only in the interest of the experiment itself, which, as we have said, would be invalidated by violent organic reactions) to ensure that the suffering undergone by these animals is reduced to the minimum.*

Pavlov was opposed to what he called "pure vivisection"—that is to say, brutal surgical intervention inflicted on an ani-

* "You ask me," Claude Bernard replied to the Académie de Médecine, "what are the main discoveries which can be credited to vivisection, and which can be used in consequence as arguments in favor of this method of study. In this connection, one need only point to the whole realm of experimental physiology. Every single one of its facts has been the direct result of vivisection. From the times of Galen, who severed the laryngeal nerves and so learned their influence on respiration and the voice; of Harvey, who discovered the circulation of the blood; or Pecquet and Aselli (the sympathetic vessels); of Haller (muscular irritability); of Bell and Magendie (the functions of the nerves)—everything has since been learned by the development of vivisection, which is the one and only experimental method; in biology, everything which is known of digestion, circulation, the liver, the sympathetic system, the bones, the development of the organism—everything, absolutely everything, is the result either of vivisection alone or of vivisection combined with other methods of study." All this remains absolutely valid today. We may note that, since approximately the time of Pasteur in France, as in the case of Claude Bernard himself, no genuine scientist has operated without anesthetizing the animal first.

* Darwin, who approved the measures taken in England to prevent cruelty to animals, wrote: "I know that physiology can make no progress if experiments on animals are forbidden. . . . Unless we are entirely ignorant of all that science has done for humanity, we must be convinced that physiology is destined to confer inestimable benefits on man and even on animals. Look at the results gained by Pasteur's work on the germs of contagious diseases: will not animals be the first to profit from them? How many lives have been saved, how much suffering has been averted, by means of experiments on animals!"

mal which had not first been anesthetized. With him, the matter was not one for emotion, but reason: "The usual method of simply vivisecting the animal in an acute experiment is, as is now becoming clearer day by day, a major source of errors, since the act of crude violation of the organism is accompanied by a mass of inhibitory influences on the functions of the different organs. . . . [This] appears to be an insurmountable obstacle to the development of synthetic physiology where it is necessary to determine exactly the true course of one or another physiological phenomenon in an intact and normal organism."

He was no sentimentalist, but he did not pretend the problem was unreal. On a monument to the dogs used in experiments, which was erected at his special request in the courtyard of the Institute of Experimental Medicine, he had these words carved: *"The dog, man's helper and friend from prehistoric times, may justly be offered as a sacrifice to science; but let this always be done without unnecessary suffering."*

TOWARD THE INTERPRETATION OF "PSYCHIC SECRETIONS"

Pursuing his experiments, Pavlov made a further operation on a dog in which a gastric fistula had already been created: he severed the esophagus in the cervical region and then fastened the two ends of the severed tube to the wound in such a way that the food, as soon as swallowed, made its way out again: instead of continuing on its journey toward the stomach, it fell out beside the dog's feeding bowl. The operation rendered possible the experiment known as "sham feeding."

This experiment made it possible to display the so-called psychic secretion in the fullest and clearest way. If the animal is offered food which it particularly likes—meat, for example—and especially if it is hungry at the time, the observer can see after some five minutes (although no food is being absorbed, since the esophagus has been severed) gastric juice beginning to flow from the miniature stomach: this is the "appetite juice" (or "psychic juice"), which possesses a high degree of proteolytic * power and which is secreted for a period varying from one to two hours.

* Proteolysis consists of hydrolysis and decomposition of proteids under the influence of soluble enzymes or of artificial chemical agents.

But gastric juice does not make its appearance only when the animal takes the food into its mouth (gustatory excitation); it appears, *in exactly the same way,* if the animal simply smells the food (olfactory excitation) or touches it with his nose (tactile excitation) or sees it (visual excitation).

At the very outset of his work, when he noted that a given food always produced the same secretion irrespective of the mode of excitation, Pavlov had said: "It is as if the glands possessed 'a kind of intelligence'." He next came to understand that the composition of the ingested food acted on the endings of the sensory nerves, which transmitted the "messages" to centers in the hindbrain; and these centers, through the mediation of the efferent nerves, triggered off the specific secretion. As he described the process, "Food excites the gustatory apparatus; the excitation is transmitted by the gustatory nerves to the medulla, from which it is conducted by the vagus nerves to the gastric glands: in other words, a reflex is produced which travels from the oral cavity to the gastric glands."

But how was the secretory mechanism to be interpreted when it was set in motion at a distance? All previous students of this "psychic secretion" had simply postulated that it arose in the "inner world" of the animal; that the animal's "desires" or "ideas" made it salivate as a man does whose "mouth waters" at the smell, sight or thought of an inviting meal.

Like his predecessors, Pavlov at first admitted the existence of a "psychic factor" capable of causing secretion at a distance: "I could not ignore," he wrote, "what was called at that time the psychic excitation of the salivary glands: a secretion stimulated, both in hungry animals and in man, by the mere sight of food, by conversation or even a thought—especially as I myself had established by precise means the existence of psychic excitation of the stomach."

But such a vague explanation as "psychic manifestation," for a phenomenon he could see happening in front of him, was not enough to satisfy such a mind as his, accustomed to the determinism of Botkin, his master, and full of adoration for Sechenov, whom he himself described as "the father of Russian physiology" and in whose eyes all subjectivism was suspect. It seemed to him that he must solve the problem as a physiologist, not as a psychologist, despite the opposition of several of his collaborators—notably Dr. Snarsky, who had to leave Pavlov's laboratory "because he persisted in adopting a subjective point of view, and because I was alarmed by the fancifulness and scientific barrenness of such a point of view."

It was with a new collaborator, Dr. Tolochinov, that he resolved to follow the new line of research which was to lead him to success: "After a veritable intellectual struggle," he wrote, "I decided that with regard to the so-called psychic excitation I would remain in the role of the pure physiologist—that is to say, of an objective observer and an experimenter taking into account nothing but external phenomena and the relationships between them. . . . For a long time, in the early days of our work, we still had the habit of discussing our subject from a psychological point of view. If our objective study met with an obstacle, or if it was slowed down because of the complexity of the phenomena under investigation, involuntary doubts at once arose as to the value of our new methods. But little by little, as our work progressed, such doubts appeared more and more rarely, and today I am convinced profoundly, once and for all, that it is by following this road that human intelligence will triumph over the most important of the problems which it is faced with solving—namely, the knowledge of the laws and mechanisms of human nature."

There is no need to be surprised that such a declaration should be the outcome of a simple study of glandular secretions. This study was only the modest, but indispensable, point of departure for much wider researches, which, by establishing more exactly the relations between stimulus, excitation and response, were to lead to an understanding of the fact that thanks to the possession of sensory receptor organs, integrative structures, and executive organs, intra-organic and extra-organic relationships were set up in the form of *reflex* actions:

"[When] one studies [the salivary glands], organs which apparently play a very insignificant physiological role . . . one cannot but be amazed by the high degree of their adaptability.

"Give the animal dry, hard food substances and there will be an abundant salivary secretion—give it liquid food and the secretion will be much smaller.

"It is obvious that for the chemical testing of the food, for mixing it and converting it into a lump to be swallowed, water is required—and the salivary glands supply it. From the mucous salivary glands there flows for every kind of food, saliva rich in mucin—a lubricating saliva, which facilitates the smooth passage of the food into the stomach. All highly irritant substances, such as acids, salts, etc., also produce a salivary secretion which varies in accordance with the strength of their stimulating action; clearly, as we know from everyday experience, the purpose of this secretion is to neutralize or dilute the substances and to cleanse the mouth. In this case the mucous glands secrete fluid saliva containing little mucin. For what would be the purpose of the mucin here? If pure insoluble quartz pebbles are placed in the mouth of a dog it will move them around, try to chew them, and, finally, it will drop them. There is either no flow of saliva at all, or at most two or three drops flow out. Again, what purpose would the saliva serve here? The pebbles are easily ejected by the animal and nothing remains in the mouth. But if sand is placed in the dog's mouth, i.e. the same pebbles, but in pulverized form, there will be an abundant flow of saliva. It is clear that without saliva, without fluid in the oral cavity, the sand could neither be ejected, nor forwarded to the stomach.

"Here we have exact and constant facts—facts *which seem to imply intelligence*."

We have italicized the last part of the sentence. Here indeed is an undeniably physiological phenomenon, since in the dog, as in other animals (including man), it takes place independently of the subject's volition; and this physiological phenomenon has all the appearances of a phenomenon of "thought." The thing happens in such a way that the gland seems *capable* of logical reasoning. If we think of the problem subjectively we find ourselves concluding that the glandular reaction must be closely related to one or another of the various operations in present-day life which we regard as being most highly "intellectualized": we see the secretion faced by a problem, analyzing the data, and giving the correct answer.

In our contemporary world, an astonishing analogy does indeed present itself to the mind: that of electronic control mechanisms. But in Pavlov's day no one had come near conceiving these marvels of cybernetic technique, which some people boldly—and quite arbitrarily—call "thinking machines," and which have become a fertile source of inspiration to the most eminent physiologists of the nervous system.

NEW TRIBULATIONS AND FINAL SUCCESS

From this point onward we shall abandon the chronological framework. Already, in fact, we have overstepped the period of Pavlov's work in Botkin's laboratory, since the complete study of glandular secretions and the reflex processes provoking them required twenty years of patient research. In addition to this study, he undertook various other investigations, which will be recapitulated briefly at the end of the book.

It was at the beginning of 1890 that Pavlov began to interest himself seriously in the phenomenon of "psychical excitation," and in consequence it was at about this time that he passed almost entirely from the study of the physiology of digestion to that of the physiology of the brain. The preceding years had seen almost no improvement in his financial situation. Professor Chistovich, who worked under him in the laboratory of Botkin's clinic, recalls: "At one juncture Pavlov found himself completely without money and had to part from his family again, and while his wife and their second son took refuge with relations he himself went to live in the apartment of his friend, Simanovski. His pupils, of whom I was one, knowing under what material difficulties he was struggling, decided to help him. We invited him to give a course of lectures on the innervation of the heart, and on the pretext of covering the expenses entailed by these lectures gave him a sum of money we had collected among ourselves. Our trouble was in vain; he spent the whole sum on experimental animals for the lectures, and kept nothing for himself."

Pavlov was used to privation. He even relates, with a certain bitterness, that he had to pay out of his own pocket for every animal used. He adds humorously: "At that time dogs were collected with the help of street thieves, who used to steal those with collars as well as those without. No doubt we shared the onus of the sin with the thieves. . . ."

By the time he was forty-one Pavlov wanted a more secure position. He put in for the post of Professor of Physiology at the University of St. Petersburg, but was turned down. Soon afterward came another setback: Delianov, one of the most reactionary of Russia's Ministers of Education, refused to confirm his appointment to a similar post in the University of Tomsk, and gave the job to the protégé of a fellow minister.

This was such an open piece of favoritism that it called forth a number of protests in medical circles. The journal *Vratch* ("Physician") compared the merits of the two candidates, to Pavlov's advantage: "We can only express our sincere regret that Ivan Petrovich Pavlov, who is responsible for private instruction in physiology at the Academy of St. Petersburg, and who was the likeliest candidate, has not been appointed to the post at Tomsk," concluded the author of the article. "Professor Pavlov has long borne the reputation of being one of our best physiologists, and his nomination had much to recommend it. He is not only a Doctor of Medicine but a Candidate of Natural Sciences, and his competence is superior to that of Doctor of Science Veliki. He has been operating at S. Botkin's clinic for several years, and his rejection for the post at Tomsk has offended so expert a judge as Sechenov himself."

Finally, despite his being a physiologist, Pavlov obtained a chair in *pharmacology* at the University of Tomsk, soon afterward another, and yet a third (also in pharmacology, not physiology) at the Military Medical Academy in St. Petersburg. As a last resort he accepted the latter and stayed in it for five years, until, in 1895, there came his long-overdue appointment to a chair in physiology at the same Academy.

He held this post uninterruptedly for thirty years. But he did other things concurrently: he organized a physiology department at the Institute of Experimental Medicine and was in charge of it until his death—that is to say, for forty-five years; his most important research was all done at this Institute.

In 1901 Pavlov was elected a corresponding member of the Académie des Sciences, but was not made a full member until 1907, despite having received in the interim the supreme international accolade in the form of the Nobel Prize (1904).

Like all other recipients of the prize, Pavlov went to Stockholm to be officially presented by the King with the diploma and the sum of money which accompanied it. Oscar II, having heard of the outstanding ability of this particular prize-winner, was anxious to receive him in private audience, but seemed so disappointed afterward that one of his intimates inquired whether "this man Pavlov was less interesting than he had been made out":

"Not at all," said the monarch naïvely, "he's a remarkable man—but he doesn't wear any decorations; he must be a socialist!"

2

Reflexes Unconditioned and Conditioned

WE have seen that Pavlov had clearly demonstrated the glands' "faculty of adaptation" to excitation arising from different substances. But what was the origin of a phenomenon which bore so marked a resemblance to intelligent thought? A difficult question. Only one thing seemed certain: in every case, glandular secretion was determined by one or more *reflex* actions.

We must first explain what a *simple* reflex is, by describing an experiment that has been carried out over and over again in laboratories in every part of the world. We take a decerebrate frog (that is, a frog from which the brain has been removed) and suspend it by the mouth from a hook; its legs hang down inertly and it shows no reactions. If we pinch a toe of one of its hind feet, we shall see that the foot is withdrawn: we have elicited a muscular response to a sensory excitation.

Now let the spinal marrow be destroyed with a scalpel. If we subsequently pinch the toe, there will be no movement; the frog will remain completely inert. The same negative reaction will be obtained if we leave the spinal marrow intact and sever the nerves connecting it with the member to be excited.

We draw the conclusion that the nerves transmit both the excitation and the response, and that the marrow is an organ capable of transforming the sensation received into a motor of command to the muscles.

A highly "intelligent" thing, the marrow! Of what mysterious stuff, then, is it made? It is very much the same as the other parts of the body: it consists of cells, and the fact that these cells are "specialized" and can be called "neurons" (every nerve cell is a neuron) makes little difference to the question, since the neurons resemble other cells at least to the extent of being built of simple "organic matter," which is an agglomerate of molecules; and these in their turn are built up of atoms which are perfectly identical with those of which inorganic matter is composed.

But inorganic matter consists of static molecules (the atoms, however, are in perpetual motion—indeed, this is what renders stable the various force effects insuring their reciprocal relationships). The molecules constituting organic matter, on the other hand, and consequently their atoms, are continually being exchanged for others. They enter from the external medium by way of nutrition and respiration, and go back to it by way of excretion.

Such exchanges, which are characteristic of life as such, take place exclusively in accordance with the laws of physics and chemistry: which is to say that they produce heat and electricity through *liberation of energy*. They enable cell tissue to keep on renewing itself, multiplying itself rapidly so that each and every cell can be replaced when damaged or worn out. We should note that nerve cells are different in this respect: they are too complex to be duplicated when required, and once they degenerate they cannot be restored. Only their processes (in the anatomical sense; that is to say, their protuberances) have the power of "growing again."

Living matter is infinitely complex, but when we resolve it into its basic structure we find only one thing: atoms, whose connections with one another are strictly subject to chemical and physical laws, and which are not static, like the atoms of mineral substances, but essentially dynamic. We can understand nothing about the phenomenon of *life* unless we have first delivered ourselves from the idea that life can be imagined as something separate from other material manifestations. Biological laws are an extension of physical and chemical laws, but they remain completely dependent on energy, from which arise the various force effects necessary for the stability of nucleus, atom, molecule and cell. It is through the development of complex from elementary structures, a development which took place through the geological ages within the framework of the evolution of species, that life rises above the condition of inertia—*from which, however, it never cuts itself free*, for it draws from that condition the resources ensuring its own permanence, and those enabling it to manifest the most recently developed aspect of its own activity, namely psychical or mental activity.

Metabolism is the name given collectively to the biochemical activities of the cellular structures comprising the organism. Metabolism is the process under which are effected the continual exchanges of which we spoke a little earlier. These exchanges involve liberations of energy causing an *electrical effect*; and on this foundation rests not only the perpetual exchange of atoms for atoms and molecules for molecules (itself a primordial feedback process), but also the possibility of transmitting sensory messages, of transcribing and integrating them, and of producing adequate responses to them.

We are still a long way from any deep understanding of psychical activity (the act of awareness and the various other phenomena of thought), an activity dependent on biological complexity and the ever closer relationships which this complexity permits between the internal and external media of individuals. But we are beginning to find ourselves quite at home with the *mechanism* of this activity, and well able to describe its elementary structures.

Thus, for example, the neuron, like all cells, is seen to be a functional unit which, naturally, has a nucleus (all cells have one, except some of the blood cells); in the nucleus we find not only the nucleoli, but also deoxyribonucleic acid, the basic constituent of the chromosomes, whose dynamical function is to shape the various morphological and physiological differentiations of the individual.

The nucleus is surrounded by cytoplasm; this contains various islands, some of which are inert and provide reserves of nourishment for the cell, while others (the centrosome, chondriosome, etc.) are alive. The cell is bounded by a membrane which is electrically polarized and therefore permeable, allowing exchanges of matter to take place between the cell and the surrounding medium.

The cytoplasm of the neurons is drawn out into *nervous fibers*; some of these are *centripetal* and are called *dendrites* (treelike in form and mostly short); others are *centrifugal* and are called *axons* (mostly unramified, and sometimes very long).

The action of the dendrites and the axons is described as centripetal and centrifugal respectively with reference to the direction taken by the *nervous impulse*: centripetal *toward* the soma (body) of the neuron, centrifugal *away from* the soma of the neuron.

Nervous influx is not so much a thing in itself as an *effect* arising from actions exerted on the sensory receptors (which are connected to the nerve endings) or on the nerves themselves. These actions may be mechanical (as when the frog's toe was pinched), or chemical (as by the introduction of an acid), or physical (as by a bombardment of photons, electrons, etc.). Their effect is to bring about a momentary change of sign in the membranous cell wall, which is electrically positive with respect to the nerve fibers and the soma of the cell, and this negative charge is then carried from the point of excitation along the axons or dendrites at speeds varying according to the thickness of the fiber, while the parts previously rendered negative by the mechanical, physical or chemical disturbance to which they were subjected regain their positive state and at the same time become metabolically active.

The wave of nervous energy is not an electric current. The nerve is not a passive electrical conductor: the nervous impulse consists of a wave of depolarization in the living medium, which in effect, the neuron constitutes.

In a nerve which has been isolated for experimental purposes, the wave can be made to travel in either direction indifferently (as can an electric current in a wire). Such is not the case in a nerve constituting an organic circuit; instead of being joined by connections (like those made in assembling some electrical apparatus or other), each neuron is separated from the next by one or more *synapses*.

The impulse could not traverse the synapses were it not for certain chemical mediators, such as acetylcholine, released by a reaction which is triggered off by the arrival of the impulse itself. The synapses prevent the impulse from being propagated in all directions, aimlessly; traffic through the synapses is one way only, passing from the axon of one neuron to the dendrites of the second and from these dendrites to the soma, from which it continues along the axons to other dendrites, and so on.* (We have deliberately omitted numerous details, and overlooked certain exceptions to the general rule.)

It can thus be seen that the dendrites are centripetal, transmitting the impulse from their own extremities to the cell soma; whereas the axons are centrifugal, transmitting it from the soma to their extremities.

It should be noted that in many cases the axons are covered with a substance called myelin in the form of a white *medullary sheath*, whose function is much more than that of a mere insulator. The somata and dendrites have no such sheath. It is mainly the somata, and their dendritic prolongations, which form the *gray matter* of the nervous center; consequently, it is of a similar gray matter that the motor centers of the spinal cord are composed (and other centers, notably those of the cortex). To close this very summary description of the essential components of the nervous system, we should add that the form and size of neurons and their processes vary a good deal, but their basic structure is the same in all cases.

Two most important points about the genesis of a nervous impulse remain to be mentioned: the nerve will not react unless a certain threshold of excitation is attained; below that threshold nothing is registered; above it, a more powerful excitation does not engender a correspondingly more powerful impulse. This is the *law of all or nothing.*

Any excitation is followed by a short lapse of time, during which the nerve is incapable of being excited; this is the *refractory period*. It seems highly probable that this time lapse is used by the cell to establish its polarity, after a surge of metabolic activity.

STRUCTURE OF THE REFLEX ARC

Let us think again of the experiment of the decerebrate frog, whose foot we pinched and which responded by withdrawing the foot. The movement of the impulse was a simple inward and outward journey, with the significant difference that the message was transformed into a response at the

* "The synapses act like valves allowing impulses to pass in one direction only . . . a rule which was called by Sherrington '*the law of forward direction*' " (Lovatt Evans, *Principles of Human Physiology*, London: J. and A. Churchill, 9th ed., 1945). (*Tr.*)

"hinge," the spinal medulla. This is an *absolute reflex*.

In principle, three neurons are sufficient to account for the structure of such a *"reflex arc"*: a *sensor* neuron, a *connector* neuron and a *motor* neuron.

The sensor neuron receives the excitation and transmits it to the connector neuron, which receives and registers it and produces the response, which is then transmitted to the muscles by the motor neuron.

In reality, of course, things are by no means so simple. To begin with, it is usually a whole chain of *affector* neurons which transmits the excitation received by the sense organs (eyes, ears, tactile papillae, etc.) to *nervous centers* consisting of a large number of anastomosed neurons, and it is also usually a chain of *effector* neurons which sets off the specific responses in the muscles, glands, etc.; but the schematic design of the arc is as we have described it: sensor-connector-motor.

We must always remember that the neuron does not behave as a passive conductor; it is active, and this applies not only to those neurons which transmit excitations or responses, but also to the neurons in the centers.

One of these centers is the spinal cord; others are in the brain, and some idea of their extreme complexity is given when we say that the number of neurons forming the cortex is in the region of 40 billion.

In the present state of our knowledge there can be no thought of describing "what goes on in the centers." In general, we can say that their working recalls that of an electronic computer—a device which functions strictly in accordance with the conditions imposed by its own construction, and responds logically to problems posed in terms of those conditions; and which also possesses a "memory." This "memory," which retains impressions made by previous operations, consists of magnetic drums or other components more or less similar to those used in instruments of the tape-recorder type (which could be made to register and reproduce visual images as well as sounds).

But analogy does not mean identity; even the most complex electronic computer is, in comparison with the most primitive living organism, an extremely simple assembly of passive conductors and other components—all the more so in comparison with organisms possessing a highly developed nervous system, in which each center itself is a "computer" influenced by other computers (other centers and other neurons), and itself influencing those computers, in other words continually modifying its own reactions by feedback effects!

Furthermore, a computer (in the ordinary sense) functions only in a strictly determined way, since its designer has taken care to keep out any external influences which might disturb and distort its operations.

It is, of course, perfectly possible to "cheat"—to construct electronic machines that seem to elude mechanical determinism (Ashby's homeostat is still the archetypal model in this field); but these are merely devised in such a way as to demonstrate that if a structure is sufficiently complex it can register different responses to identical excitations; and the potentialities of these ingenious devices are soon exhausted. No amount of extrapolation will alter the fact that the robot can only solve problems; it can never set them.

But the analogy between computer and nervous system is nonetheless a very instructive one. It gives us the key to the general means by which the organism keeps itself in harmony with its various media, and it proves to us how much of our behavior depends on reflex actions. The very recent discovery of the semi-conducting qualities of certain cellular components (notably DNA, or deoxyribonucleic acid, the main ingredient of chromosomes), qualities like those of the magnetic memories used in various kinds of electronic apparatus, also gives us reason to hope that we may lift at least a corner of the veil of mystery which lies over the phenomena of remembering—the phenomena governing, in all likelihood, the "circumstantial responses" of the centers.

MEMORY AND REFLEXES

Memory is a biological process rendered possible by the fact that organic structures contain ferromagnetic or ferroelectric substances which receive, retain and reproduce impressions in a manner more or less comparable with that exploited by electronic engineers; that is to say, a manner dependent on electromagnetism. Memory occurs even at the cellular level—though, it is true, in a simple, rudimentary fashion. Unicellular animals display memory, despite their lack of any sort of a nervous system; under the influence of physical or chemical stimuli they show themselves capable of a kind of "apprenticeship to life." It really seems as if excitations, once having evoked a response other than those innate in the creature, are capable of leaving an "imprint," so that the creature begins to possess "acquired reflexes" as well as innate.

A similar phenomenon, on a much ampler scale, is found in organisms possessed of nervous systems. But in these organisms, the building up of memory traces seems to depend on large and complex processes of induction, involving not just a single nerve cell or even a number of nerve centers but vast patterns of functioning evoked by identical excitations and developing in space and time—in other words, dynamically.

The phenomenon of memory can be seen to form part not only of acquired but also of innate reflexes. Innate reflexes seem to be transmitted by means of the chromosomes; if this is really true, then we must admit the reality of inherited memories. Perhaps, as Pavlov believed, conditioned actions turn into instincts if the conditioning is administered to a sufficient number of generations in succession. But this is extremely far from being certain.

Only innate factors are indisputably hereditary. Automatisms such as the one whose mechanism we reviewed earlier (flexion of a limb in the decerebrate frog, following excitation by pinching), a reaction which is found in all quadrupeds and depends only on the spinal medulla, is an example of a very simple innate reflex. Other, hardly more complicated reflexes depend on centers situated higher in the neuraxis. (The neuraxis is the spinal medulla and the encephalon together, that is to say the spinal cord *plus* the various parts of the brain.) One such case is that of the salivary and gastric reflexes, in which the mechanism of response to excitation has its seat in the hindbrain. If we sever the vagus nerves, in other words those which emerge from the medulla oblongata and innervate the greater part of the thoracic and abdominal viscera, we shall find that excitations which formerly produced a flow of gastric juice now no longer produce it.

There are other innate reflexes of a far more complex nature, depending on the interaction of several centers; either a positive interaction (eliciting a function or a movement) or negative (inhibiting a function or movement). This is the case with the highly complicated nerve network which governs vegetative functioning, and in whose activities the will does not intervene under normal conditions.

Until fairly recently the vegetative nervous system (which is divided into the sympathetic and parasympathetic systems) was called the "independent nervous system." But while the sympathetic, with its intricate network of nerves and ganglia, appears to be anatomically independent of the neuraxis, dissection shows its ganglia to have numerous connections with the cerebro-spinal system, and also that both the sympathetic and the parasympathetic are linked with higher centers in the diencephalon.

Pavlov's successors, particularly Professors K. M. Bykov and M. A. Usievich, have shown that the vegetative system itself can provide a site for appropriate conditioned reflexes. This discovery was the start of a new, "corticovisceral" branch of physiology.

The possibility of visceral conditioning, and the mastery which in particular the yogis succeeded in obtaining over some of the organic reactions which normally elude voluntary control, incontrovertibly prove the existence of a connection between the diencephalic centers (or, to be more precise, hypothalamic centers), which regulate the sympathetic system, and the cortex.

It is impossible to overemphasize the fact that the organism is a whole, and that the nervous system is a whole. This whole, functioning by self-regulation, can nevertheless be analyzed into parts, each of which has a definite role to play in the giving and receiving of orders. Let us see what these parts of the nervous system are, and what they do.

THE NEURAXIS

The lower portion of the neuraxis is the spinal medulla: a whitish, cylindrical cord consisting of nervous processes sheathed in myelin, its center composed of gray matter, that is, of neuronic somata and of unsheathed, anastomosed neuronic processes. The spinal medulla swells out at its upper end to form the bulb known as the *medulla oblongata*, from which emerge among other nerves those which are involved in gastric secretion, as we saw previously.

Just above the medulla oblongata, but clearly distinguishable from it, is the *pons*, from the anterior surface of which there stems the bulkiest of the cranial nerves: the trigeminal, which has a multiple role, since, through the instrumentality of this center (the pons), it imparts sensibility to the face, the nasal fossae and the oral cavity, and also controls the muscles of mastication.

The pons is closely connected with the *cerebellum,* which lies behind it. The cerebellum is an important projecting structure consisting of two rounded hemispheres, consisting (except for its centers) of numerous myelinated fibers which make afferent or efferent connections with the cortex and the medulla by various paths. The cerebellum may be said to form a kind of bridge or connecting bypass with the nervous paths into and out of the brain; this enables it to act as a regulator of automatic movements, posture and balance.

The next region, in ascending order, is the *diencephalon* (often known as the midbrain), probably the most important tract of the brain in connection with the establishment of the innate reflexes, or instincts. It lies inside the masses of white matter constituting the cerebral hemispheres (forebrain).

The main components of the diencephalon are the thalamus, the hypothalamus—extending from the hypophysis, which lies endways to the pituitary gland—and finally the elusive epiphysis.

The *epiphysis* is a tiny gland, only 2 millimeters across; Descartes thought it was "the seat of the soul." Its role is as yet uncertain; probably it causes hormonal secretions of a regulating kind. On the other hand, the *hypophysis* is quite clearly an endocrine gland with a regulatory function; some have even gone so far as to call it "the endocrine brain." The hypophysis furnishes a highly complex system of feedback arrangements, receiving hormonal messages and, by means of its own hormonal secretions, regulating those of other essential organs; a task which it carries out in close collaboration with the hypothalamus.

The *hypothalamus*, consisting chiefly of gray nuclei, ensures the regulation of the vegetative nervous system, the regulation of body heat, the harmonious working of metabolic functions, and the basic nervous commands underlying instinctive behavior. It plays a part in trophism (nutrition of the tissues) and in the sexual functions. It is the center of the affective reactions (attention, pain, pleasure) and instinctive needs (hunger, thirst, sexual desire). It governs emotions and feelings (the nature of which is instinctive). In man, irritation of the hypothalamus causes intense emotional excitement; its destruction causes apathy and somnolence.

Its posterior region, in close collaboration with the formatio reticularis, plays a part in the control of sleep.

The *thalamus*, or optic layer, is the relay station for all incoming sensory impressions, with the exception of smell (which is received in the rhinencephalon). It is essentially a coordinating center for the cerebral cortex.

The *corpora striata*, the outer portion of the gray nuclei in the center of the mass of the encephalon, work in conjunction with the "red nucleus" which lies lower down, to ensure the maintenance of muscular tonus and other automatic functions.

INNATE AND ACQUIRED FACTORS

A human being born possessing only those parts of the neuraxis which we have so far described (as is the case with "anencephalic" children, so called because born without cerebral hemispheres) would be able to "live" a vegetative life, provided he was fed by other people (anencephalic children can be kept alive for several years in this way). But he would be totally incapable of taking the initiative; he could not seek food on his own account. He would be less than an animal belonging to a lower stage in the evolutionary scale, and possessing a primitive brain with the rhinencephalon as its highest component (for, in such creatures, instinct predominates over acquired tendencies throughout their span of life). It is only by instinct that they perform the actions necessary for maintaining life and reproducing their kind (though, within limits, they are also capable of acquiring new activities; for example, a unicellular animal is capable of "learning," and an earthworm, which possesses a nervous system, acquires true conditioned reflexes).

We must not rush to the conclusion that *all* reflexes involving the use of cortical pathways are acquired reflexes. The cortex also figures as an important coordinator of innate reflexes; even when it exists only in an embryonic stage of development, as in amphibians, its removal is not without effect on the animal's instinctive behavior.

Let us confine ourselves to vertebrates, because the nervous systems of invertebrates, though constructed of neurons, is rather different from our own (and also because in some invertebrates, namely the so-called "social" insects, we should have to reckon with group effects).

If the pallium of a frog is removed, but the optic layers

are left intact, the animal goes on living in a more or less normal manner, but is less adroit in capturing its prey. A snake without a cortex shows reactions which for the most part are like those of a normal snake; but it will have lost the impulse to flee when approached. A pigeon without a cortex is much more severely handicapped but is nevertheless able to live in a friendly environment, with food within its reach. A decorticate dog, on the other hand, though it keeps its affective reactions, will not eat unless its nose is thrust into the bowl containing its food. The monkey, which rarely lives long after decerebration (unlike the cat and the dog, which survive provided they are helped to eat), can only accomplish a few stereotyped actions. It will even remain plunged in deep sleep, from which it is woken only with great difficulty in order to be artificially fed. As for man, the complete absence of hemispheres plunges him into coma.

Taking a general survey of the matter, we can see a progressive shrinking of the innate, where the relationship to the environment is concerned, as we ascend from species with a lower stage of cortical development to those with a higher one. The little chick is in no need of being taught to peck at the food on which it will live throughout its life. As soon as it emerges from the egg, the alimentary reflex comes into play; a stimulus in the shape of a grain of corn, represented in the chick's vision as a light-reflected spit, is enough to evoke it at once. A mammal, it is true, sucks instinctively; its weaning, on the other hand, must undoubtedly be placed in the acquired category. Pavlov showed this very clearly by feeding puppies on milk after the suckling period was over; the sight of meat did not make them salivate, but as soon as they were made to taste meat the salivating reflex with respect to meat was fully established, and thereafter they salivated not only on direct contact with meat but also at a distance.

This, beyond doubt, was the establishment of a conditioned reflex. New paths of nervous transmission had come into play, and, as Pavlov proved, they required the activity of the cortex as an integrating center, a coordinating relay center.

THE CORTEX

The greater part of the cranial cavity is filled by the cerebral hemispheres, two distinct masses between which is the *rhi-*

nencephalon, a single mass whose special function is to integrate olfactory sensations. The two hemispheres are joined at their bases by the *corpus callosum*, which consists of thick bundles of myelinated fibers.

Most of the bulk of the two hemispheres is made up of white matter, overlaid with the gray matter of the cortex. Let us recall in passing that nerve centers are made up not only of neurons, with their processes myelinated or not, as the case may be, but also of supporting tissue, the *neurilemma*, the exact part played by which is not yet known but which has the same embryological origin as the neurons themselves.

The gray matter forming the cerebral cortex, to a depth of only 2-3 millimeters (which however does not prevent it, with its folds, from attaining a total surface area of 1,924 square centimeters), consists of six layers of different thickness, the details of whose structure we shall omit. But we must mention that the neurons constituting the cortex show considerable differences in size: they vary in length from five to a hundred thousandths of a millimeter. Morphologically, too, they vary greatly (the most striking contrast being that between the pyramidal neurons and the rest). Their dendrites are always multipolar. Their axons may be very short, in which case they are not myelinated, form part of the gray matter and do not project beyond the area occupied by the nuclei; or they may be very long, becoming myelinated as they issue from the encephalon, and terminating in (for example) the gray matter of the spinal medulla, and thus being capable of modifying the responses of medullary motor neurons (which explains why an innate reflex, like that of the "automatic" withdrawal of the frog's foot when a toe is pinched—a reflex found in all vertebrates, man of course included—can be "voluntarily" inhibited). As a general indication, we may mention that, in man, a frontal neuron terminating in the lumbar region may measure something over three feet.

The cortex has a number of circumvolutions separated by folds, furrows or clefts. The two most important of these are, on the external surface of each hemisphere, the Rolandic fissure along the center, above, and the Sylvian fissure below.*

The various regions of the cerebral cortex are divided into *lobes*. In front of the Rolandic fissure is the frontal lobe; be-

* The fissure of Rolando and the fissure of Sylvius are also known respectively as the central sulcus and the lateral sulcus (*Tr.*)

hind it, the parietal lobe. Hidden deep in the Sylvian fissure is a lobe known as the insula. The temporal lobe lies above the Sylvian fissure; at the rear end of the hemisphere is the occipital lobe. These statements apply to both hemispheres alike.

The occipital lobe is the "visual brain"; the eyes are the visual apparatus receiving the message, the optic nerves convey it from the retinas, and the occipital lobe translates it. The optic nerves cross over each other in front of the

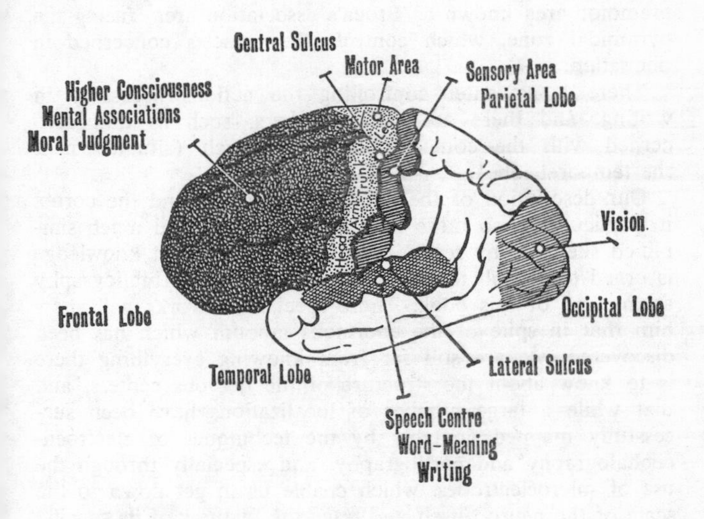

hypophysis, in the *optic chiasma*. They come together again on each side of the optic layers in the thalamus and pass from thence to the occipital lobes.

The temporal lobe is the auditive brain, responsible for translating the messages coming from the complex auditory apparatus of the ear by way of the auditory nerves.

The parietal lobe translates tactile messages originating in the skin, muscles and joints, and gustatory messages from the papillae of the oral mucosae. The parietal lobes are also the centers of general kinesthetic sensibility.

On each side of the Rolandic fissure, i.e. to the front and the rear of it, lie very important motor and sensory centers.

They are arranged from the top downward in an order corresponding to the following parts of the body (to put it in summary fashion): foot, knee, hip, trunk, neck, shoulder, elbow, hand, fingers, thumb, face, mouth, lips, tongue, jaw, pharynx, larynx. Those parts of this cortical area which correspond to relatively insensitive parts of the body are smaller in extent, and consist of fewer neurons than those corresponding to body zones endowed with high sensibility and powers of precise and delicate movement, such as thumbs and lips.

The motor center of speech is situated in a part of the premotor area known as Broca's association area, facing the pyramidal zone, which controls the muscles concerned in phonation.

There is a center controlling the actions necessary in writing; and there are various others, such as that concerned with the comprehension of speech (situated near the temporal lobe).

Our description of the neuraxis in general and the cortex in particular is no more than an elementary and much simplified sketch. Any reader who wants more exact knowledge is urged to consult the handbooks named in the bibliography at the end of this book. Those specialized works will show him that in spite of the enormous amount which has been discovered, we are still far from knowing everything there is to know about the structure of the nervous centers, and that while a large number of localizations have been successfully mapped (notably by the techniques of electroencephalography and cortiography, and especially through the use of microelectrodes, which enable us to get down to the scale of the neuron itself and trace the features of its specific activity), the functioning of the nervous system cannot be understood unless we consider the system dynamically and as a whole. More, indeed—we cannot view that system otherwise than in close connection with the organism as a whole. And more again—the functioning of the organism as a whole must be seen in the light of its environmental conditions in the broadest sense, the interweaving of physical, chemical, biological and psychological factors.

THE IMPORTANCE OF ACQUIRED BEHAVIOR

Pavlov has written: "The nervous system is the most complex and delicate instrument on our planet, by means of which relations, connections are established between the numerous parts of the organism, as well as between the organism, as a highly complex system, and the innumerable, external influences. . . . The animal organism, as a system, exists in surrounding nature thanks only to the constant equilibration of this system with the environment, i.e. thanks to definite reactions of the living system to stimulations reaching it from without, which in higher animals is effected mainly by means of the nervous system in the shape of reflexes."

Every reflex depends on the existence of the following elements: an *excitant* (or stimulus—an agent of some kind in the internal or external medium) acting on a *receptor apparatus* (tactile corpuscles or, looking at the matter on a larger scale, a whole sensory organ such as the ear, the eye, etc.) which is the starting point of a *sensory nerve* (which in many cases consists of a chain of relays) carrying the sensation to a *nervous center* (composed of innumerable anastomosed cells offering a large number of circuits to the incoming message) following which, after communication along an *efferent nerve* (a nerve transmitting the response which the center has elaborated in terms of the stored memories reactivated by the impulse), the *executive organ* (which may be a striped muscle, that of a limb for example, or the smooth muscle of one of the viscera, or a secretory gland, or a regulating relay center with activating or inhibiting action) is able to react in an adequate way.

It is essential that all these six elements (those italicized) be intact. The suppression of any one of them prevents the reflex action from developing; which is to say that no reflex could take place if there were no contact with the medium (internal or external, as the case may be) or if there were no centers, no nervous communication or no executive organs. However complex a reflex may be and however much it may increase the complexity of an organic situation, biologically or psychologically, these elementary principles always apply.

"This equilibration," Pavlov goes on to say, "and consequently, the integrity both of the individual organism and of its species, is ensured first of all by the simplest unconditioned reflexes (such as coughing when foreign substances enter the larynx), as well as by the most complex ones, which are usually known as instincts—alimentary, defensive, sexual and others. The reflexes are caused both by internal agents arising within the organism and by external agents, and this ensures the perfection of the equilibration."

Pavlov points to the analogy between this "adaptation" (maintenance of biological equilibrium) and, as he says, "what can be observed in any inanimate body." For example, a chemical mixture with a complicated formula "cannot remain in this form save through the equilibrium of its atoms and that of their groupings, and through the equilibrium between the totality of these groupings and the surrounding medium." We may add that this is equally true of astronomical structures: the equilibrium of the solar system, stellar systems, galaxies, and so on.

"But the equilibrium attained by these reflexes is complete only when there is an absolute constancy of the external environment. But since the latter, being highly varied, is always fluctuating, the unconditioned, or constant connections are not sufficient; they must be supplemented by conditioned reflexes, or temporary connections."

Let us try to summarize his thought by means of a few pertinent examples. Consider an animal other than a parasite or a protozoon, living in a permanent food-bearing environment. It is obvious that if it contents itself with merely eating whatever food is within immediate range it will be in danger of starving. It must continually go in quest of pasture, if it is herbivorous, or of prey, if carnivorous.

Hence the alimentary reflex alone is not enough. Of course the creature can wander at random and may, by pure luck, come upon the food it wants; this may well be the case of a herbivorous animal on the luxuriant pampas; but in any less opulent surroundings the possession of that single, absolute reflex will prove less than sufficient. It is imperative that some conditional stimulus, such as the *sight* of a bush, the *scent* of a flower, be present to give the necessary guidance. The animal must also possess inhibitory conditioned reflexes, to prevent it from sallying incontinently hither and thither: behind the tempting bush may lurk a beast of prey ready to pounce and devour. A suspect *rustle* among the leaves, the *sound* of which reaches the herbivore, represents the *signal* —the conditional stimulus of the inhibitory reflex—which will make the creature stop in time.

Naturally, the sight of the herbivore is itself the conditional stimulus causing the carnivore to crouch in readiness and stalk slowly and cautiously toward its prey. Reflexes—some activating, others inhibiting—are continually at work. Some reinforce innate reactions, others supplement or supplant them. Some are brought into being more or less fortuitously in the setting of what we call "experience," others originate in group or parental training. The whole represents what we call, generically, "behavior." The main incentive is food, but the situation is also one of everything which concerns the life and well-being of the organism and the perpetuation of its kind; everything, as Pavlov says, "which is to be taken from the environment or which is to be shunned or warded off."

In man—for whom, when all is said, life is not just a matter of food-getting, repose and sexual activity—the number of reflexes acquired through education, cultural association, personal experience, all the things we call our "habits" or our "way of life," is very considerable. Every day brings us new ones. Every thought causes us to create new ones. Thought itself is the source of a multitude of conditioned reflexes, more or less harmoniously interwoven and interdependent, brought into being through our power of conceptualization. Our reactions to people about us are conditioned reflexes, and this includes all our gestures of affection, including love.

"The temporary nervous connection," writes Pavlov, "is the most universal physiological phenomenon both in the animal world and in ourselves. At the same time it is a psychological phenomenon—that which the psychologists call association, whether it be combinations derived from all manner of actions or impressions, or combinations derived from letters, words and thoughts." He goes on to ask: "Are there any grounds for differentiation, for distinguishing between that which the physiologist calls the temporary connection and that which the psychologist terms association? They are fully identical; they merge and absorb each other. Psychologists themselves seem to recognize this, since they (at least, some of them) have stated that the experiments with conditioned reflexes provide a solid foundation for associative psychology, i.e. psychology which regards association as the base of psychical activity."

In what conditions, and in what way, are conditioned reflexes formed? We shall devote our next chapter to answering this question.

3

The Physiology of Behavior

DESCARTES, the real founder of scientific psychology, had clearly seen the close connection between physiological and psychological life. Though he remained fundamentally dualistic in his outlook, he declared that "even in man, the body sometimes escapes from the influence of the soul and functions merely by reflexes." He showed that the "animal spirits," passing along the channels of the nerves, could impinge on the brain and command the movements of muscles by way of other nerves.* If we substitute "nervous impulse" for "animal spirits" we shall be left with a fair description of the reflex arc.

The reality of reflex action was demonstrated about 1800, both by Charles Bell and by Magendie (the law of roots,

* René Descartes (1596–1650), French philosopher and mathematician, whose works include the *Discours de la méthode* (with its famous and much debated *Cogito ergo sum,* "I think, therefore I am") and the *Traité des passions.* On the mathematical side, his monumental achievement was the invention of analytical geometry. A less spectacular achievement was his decision to use letters near the end of the alphabet, such as *x* and *y,* for unknown quantities, and those at the beginning for known quantities—a simple convention now taken for granted by everyone. It has been claimed that without this improvement in algebraical notation the binomial theorem might well not have been detected as early as it was (that is, by Newton, 1642–1727). (*Tr.*)

still known as the Bell-Magendie law); they showed what we saw earlier in the experiment with the decerebrate frog, namely that the spinal marrow was capable of functioning as an independent center, without intervention by the brain.

Later, Hall, followed by Pflüger, and after him by Lotze, established and described the analogy existing between involuntary reflexes and voluntary actions of adaptation; without, however, allowing the possibility that will could be analyzed in terms of physiology. In 1934 the great British scientist Sherrington, the importance of whose contribution to the study of the nervous system cannot be overestimated, declared: "Aristotle wondered in what way the mind was connected with the body. We are still asking ourselves the same question."

The problem is, in very truth, extremely complex. There can be no doubt that reflexes constitute a means by which psychic life is externalized; but they are not psychic life itself. Pavlov, unlike some of his successors, was careful to refrain from rash extrapolation. He even said, "Our behavior is far from being merely a sum of reflexes," and we shall see that he himself called attention to a remarkable case of animal intelligence, one transcending the reflex framework.

But the fact remains that psychical activities are determined by the interactions of the living creature, as subject, with the objective world. There are not two things, a biological complex in constant interaction with the physical world, and an independent psychical entity; there is one thing, a functional whole whose reactions it is possible to study in terms of physiology.

We most certainly do not claim to explain the *essence* of primordial energy and its condensation into material particles at a point in space-time, by enunciating the laws of physics and chemistry which enable us to analyze the force effects engendered by the movements of matter. Nor are we sufficiently bold (or unthinking) to imagine that by showing how psychical activity is externalized we are also showing what it essentially is.

As the Soviet psychologist Rubinstein put it: "Insofar as they obey the physiological laws of nervous activity (the dynamical laws of the nervous processes), psychological phenomena appear to be the outcome of physiological laws; while biological (and therefore physiological) phenomena themselves appear to be the outcome of the physicochemical laws determining the movements of material particles."

What is energy? What is mind? We do not know. We can see that the first underlies the structure of matter and of its movements, while the second seems to be the final result of the dynamic complexification of material structures. We also observe that the possibility exists of wider and deeper contacts with the universe, by virtue of this very complexification; and it is clear to us that this contact results in "something" which is not material, but spiritual. We can see no more—and no less!

According to Aristotle, the seat of the mind was the heart. The Stagirite regarded the brain as merely an organ for "cooling the fluids of the body." Nevertheless, he did not consider the soul to be an isolated entity; he saw it as being in some way the "form" on which the body was "molded."

The idea of a formal separation between body and soul was first maintained by Descartes, and only with reference to man; he considered animals to be like machines.

We have seen that Descartes was not content merely to point to the brain as the seat of the entity called soul, but that he situated it much more exactly, in the epiphysis. Leibniz, though also a dualist, advanced a very different conception. While, in his view, there was no causal relationship between body and soul, so that their activities were at all times independent of one another, they were nonetheless subject to parallel laws: every mental event reflected a physiological event. A similar conception is found in Locke and even in Wundt, the founder of experimental psychology.

In spite of its essentially dualistic nature, this conception of psycho-physical parallelism did encourage an admission that physiological experiment offered a chance for the study of psychological effects (because the laws of causation in both were identical). Wundt, in fact, chose the title *Physiological Psychology* for his first book.

Like Pavlov, Wundt was a physiologist. With such a background, and given that he accepted parallelism, one might have expected to find him doing the logical thing and conducting his work under the aegis of physiology. But he did nothing of the kind. His psycho-physiology was entirely based on introspection and he reasoned from human to animal experience, thus stultifying his work—which, however, is far from being valueless. As Professor Henri Piéron has said he "advanced in reverse gear." It is an inescapable rule in psychology, as in all other disciplines, that the higher cannot be explained save by starting from the lower. Which is why Professor Piéron, an animal psychologist of worldwide reputation, has always refused to discuss the essential nature of psychic life, confining himself to the study of psychic life as an immediate fact.

He is, with Pavlov, and with Watson (the founder of *behaviorism*), one of the first psychologists to have resolutely abandoned the dualist thesis (separation of body and soul) in favor of a thoroughgoing monism. And, as a scrupulous experimentalist, he has refused to let himself be labeled a materialist, though there is no doubt that he is an uncompromising rationalist. He has said, substantially, that "we have to rid ourselves of all prejudices, all tendencies, all metaphysical preoccupations, whether they lean toward idealism or materialism; above all, of course, we have to free ourselves of religious dogma."

This declaration puts Professor Piéron much closer to the dialectical materialism of Pavlov (whose ideas, moreover, he has done much to disseminate in France) than to the mechanistic materialism of Watson, whose excesses he has deplored, while praising the scientific rigor with which the behaviorists conduct their experiments.

To the behaviorists, in fact, "what we call mind is only the behavior of the organism." There are signal-stimuli from the external world on the one hand, and the organism's responses on the other (the behaviorists have made admirable use of the Pavlovian doctrine of reflexes); and that is all. "The organism, by means of its responses," said Watson in effect, "modifies its physiological state in such a way that the stimulus ceases to cause a reaction. Thus stimulation breaks up a state of equilibrium, which the response restores. Since stimulation from the environment is continuous the organism must continuously maintain its equilibrium by producing responses, and thus the individual is always 'doing something.' " The behaviorists also maintain that the nervous system invariably functions in complete arcs—in other words, they admit only the reflex as the type of nervous activity and deny the existence of any independent cortical activity.

However satisfactory this point of view may be in accounting for the main activities of men and animals, it is strikingly inadequate as an explanation of the many phenomena which we feel to be primarily mental, such as the act of awareness, not to mention intuition and creative thought, which in many if not all cases depend finally on culture—a highly advanced form of conditioning.

Mechanistic materialism, as the present writer has often maintained, claims finality without being aware of doing so. It tends for example to reduce evolution to a mere collection of chance events, which would seem in any case to be contrary not only to observation, but even to statistical probability. But if we find it possible to maintain that even environmental factors can be accounted for inside the mechanistic framework, or at least that they are bound by biological determinism and hence by physical and chemical laws, we are still faced with an apparent exception as soon as psychical activity comes on to the scene—the exception being *the possibility of a response to new situations.* And, unless we have made up our minds to adhere systematically to the statistical approach, we shall find ourselves confronted by a further highly significant state of affairs; the possibility of different individuals giving *different responses to identical situations*, or, even more significantly, of the same individuals giving varied responses in similar situations.

Does "freedom of choice" really exist in such cases, or must we admit that we are the victims of an illusion—that, for example, there exist causes of interference which elude our inadequate powers of observation? Everything inclines us to believe that freedom to choose, however microscopic it may be, is a reality; but let us remain sufficiently cautious and humble to admit that no really satisfying answer can be given in the present state of our knowledge.

Pavlov disliked any talk of "freedom of choice"; he felt the notion offended against scientific rigor. He has nevertheless shown how the mounting complexity of systems and interactions resulted eventually in something which is more than a mere mechanism: *intelligence.* Here is his own account of an undeniable example of animal intelligence.

We must explain that when a fistula is set up for experimental purposes, ulceration is sometimes caused by the repeated action of the acid digestive juices on the operational wound:

"In one of the dogs operated according to our method the eroding action of the juice began to manifest itself ten to fifteen days after the operation. The dog was tied in the laboratory. One morning, much to our annoyance, a heap of plaster torn from the wall was found beside the animal which was generally known for its quiet behavior. The dog was then chained in another part of the room. Next morning we observed the same thing—another part of the wall had been damaged. At the same time it was noticed that the dog's abdomen was dry and that the cutaneous irritation had considerably diminished. Only then did we realize what had caused the dog's strange behavior. The animal had found a way of arresting the irritation and, in fact, of healing itself. Through its intelligence, it had helped not only itself, but us. We then prepared a bed of sand for the dog (other porous materials, such as plaster or sawdust, can be used), and from that time onward there was no more damage to the wall and no more irritation of the skin, as the porous medium absorbed the juice."

Have not we all noticed equally surprising behavior on the part of animals? And do not these contrasts, these sudden brief escapes from the realm of reflex action, show us the true face of psychical activity?

HOW A CONDITIONED REFLEX IS CREATED

Let us return to an example we have already mentioned, and which served as a basis for much of Pavlov's experimenting. We have preferred it to a number of others because it presents parallels to the conditions surrounding animals in the natural state.

Consider a puppy that has been weaned, but that has been carefully kept away from all food except milk. It does not salivate at the sight of meat, and if our thinking is subjective we shall say that this is "because he doesn't know what meat is." When he was born he sucked without being taught, and we say that the cause was an *instinct* or an *innate reflex* or, more accurately, a combination of more complicated innate reflexes than the simple *absolute reflex* which makes the decerebrate frog withdraw its foot when a toe is pinched.

We now put a bit of meat into our puppy's mouth. At once, just as when he first fed on milk, he begins salivating. Here again an innate reflex is in action, and indeed we can pronounce it to be an absolute reflex because it requires the activity of only one nervous center. When the puppy starts to chew, we are of course witnessing a combination of innate reflexes, with different centers as their respective origins; and the coordination of these reflex actions no doubt demands the work of one or several other centers, but we can overlook that for the time being.

Let us concentrate on the ground plan of the absolute reflex, that of salivation, ignoring all else. We see that the action of—

(*a*) the *excitant* or stimulus (meat) on

(*b*) the *lingual papillae* (sensory receptors), followed by the carrying of the nervous impulse thus created along

(*c*) the *fibers of the lingual nerve* (centripetal path of gustatory excitation) toward

(*d*) the *medullary center* (which integrates the sensation, interprets it, and initiates the appropriate response), brings about, by means of a new nervous impulse traveling along

(*e*) the *chorda tympani* (centrifugal path), secretion from

(*f*) the *submaxillary gland.*

Of course, all this is schematic and greatly oversimplified; we have omitted all mention of relays and made no distinction between the various parts of the internal surfaces of the mouth which are capable of setting the secretory process in motion; but our sketch will at any rate serve as a working hypothesis.

As soon as he has tasted meat, though it be only a few times or even once, our puppy will salivate *merely at the sight of meat*, its *smell,* etc. Our schematic outline is no longer adequate: (*a*) an *optical excitant* (the meat, as before, but merely seen, not placed in the mouth) acting on (*b*) the *retinas* (sensory receptors) causes a message to be sent along (*c*) the *optic nerve* to (*d*) the *visual centers* (in the occipital lobes), which recognize the excitant correctly and, by the appropriate nervous paths, initiate in the medullary center a response identical with that produced more directly on the first occasion, when the meat was placed in the puppy's mouth.

This second sketch is really more grossly oversimplified than the first, but it does give us an approximate picture of the nature of "psychical" salivation and also of the simplest type of conditioned reflex.

The message *conditioning* the psychical salivation, that is to say the meat presented without contact, would have produced the result equally efficiently by means of its smell, as we mentioned above. In that case the puppy would have "recognized" the meat with his eyes bandaged, and the main integrating center would have been the rhinencephalon. Similar examples can be adduced to show transposition to any of the senses.

Something to be borne in mind is that several agents of excitation, and consequently several sensory organs, may participate in the formation of a single conditioned reflex as simple as the one just described. This means that the dog may simultaneously see, smell and touch the meat (with his nose) and produce psychical salivation, which in this case does not involve direct nervous pathways (lingual papillae-afferent nerves-medullary center-efferent nerves-salivary glands), but indirect pathways and a complex circuit (sensory receptors not specific to salivation, afferent nerves leading to the integrating center in the cortex, efferent nerves from this center to the locality of the absolute reflex, etc.).

Nor is this all. Till now, the conditional excitant, or stimulus, has acted directly on the sensory areas not specifically connected with salivation, just as it acts directly on the apparatus which *is* specifically connected with salivation, in the mechanism of the absolute reflex. But the absolute stimulus, which has become conditional and acts in that case at a distance, is not even necessary for the provocation of a salivary reflex (or a gastric one). The conditional stimulus can be anything whatsoever—not necessarily meat—provided that it has been associated a certain number of times with the original stimulus (meat).

Thus, provided that a few seconds before offering meat to a dog (which will excite the absolute reflex of salivation), we excite one of its neutral receptors (i.e. a receptor not connected with salivation) by means of a neutral stimulus, we shall subsequently obtain, by presenting the conditional stimulus alone, a secretion identical with that produced by the absolute stimulus. More concretely: if, three or four seconds before placing meat in a dog's mouth, we cause him to hear a noise, or see something, or smell something, or feel contact of some kind, we shall thereafter elicit salivation by the use of such a conditional stimulus alone, without the absolute stimulus (the meat).

How does this come about?

THE CEREBRAL MOSAIC

Before we study *how* a conditioned reflex is created, let us consider *where* this creation takes place: namely, in the cortex and its 14 billions or so of neurons.

Like all cells, the neurons are perpetually exchanging materials with the surrounding medium in a more or less direct way. This biochemical activity (metabolism) produces energy. In what concerns our own subject (higher nervous activity), the essential effect of metabolism is to maintain the electrical polarity of the superficial membranes of the neuron and its processes (they tend to be positively electrified: their constituent elements are deficient in electrons).

But a neuron is not an isolated entity. When the organism as a whole is in the waking state, each neuron is in constant touch with the organism, which is itself in touch with the surrounding medium. The neurons in the nervous centers are particularly subject to a host of reciprocal interactions. It would, indeed, be hard not to realize that electric potentials must vary as a result of the manifold influences passing between neurons and neurons and between other structures and neurons: impulses arriving rhythmically at the synapses, chemical modifications caused by various secretions (notably those of the hormones), physical effects of fields of force, and so on.

Whenever depolarization has the upper hand (local increase in the number of electrons), the neuron sends nervous impulses along its axon (later, in studying sleep, we shall see that enhanced polarization has the effect of insulating the neuron). It may be noted in passing that according to present ideas a large part of the functioning of the neurons in the cortical centers depends simply on the interplay of waves of polarization and depolarization, not necessarily occasioned by any message from afferent nerves.

Since Hans Berger's work, which has been the foundation of the extraordinary development of electroencephalography (EEG) and electrocorticography, it has been possible to register and record the fluctuating pulsations, some synchronized and others not, emanating from the neurons of the brain. Without going into technical details, we may say that these instruments as used in the laboratory are not "thought-reading machines," as some people have taken it on themselves to call them, but devices that register variations in electric potentials, these latter being considerably amplified so as to make them easier to read. In addition, the use of microelectrodes is leading to more and more precise investigation, rendering it possible to concentrate on a single neuron or even on its nucleus. It is possible not only to collect, metaphorically speaking, the electricity emitted by the centers—that is, to record differences in potential caused by the neurons' activity—but also directly to excite the centers (or any one neuron, or one of its processes, or any sense organ) by means of an electric current extraneous to the organism.

First example: using electrodes that transmit differences in potential caused by cellular activity, we obtain the encephalogram of a subject whom we have asked to lie on a couch, relaxing as deeply as possible and "thinking of nothing." Let us say that we succeed in recording the regular rhythms of the occipital *alpha*-waves. We now ask the subject to open his eyes; and we observe a sudden change (block) in the rhythm, whose amplitude has greatly decreased. This change is caused by the disturbance to the "resting activity" of the centers concerned, a disturbance brought about by the wave of nervous input initiated by the action of photons on the retinas.

Second example: a patient whose cranium has been opened by surgery, the brain being thus exposed. We can plant electrodes on any part of its surface (this causes no pain whatsoever). If we excite a motor area with a weak electric current we shall see the patient make involuntarily some movement which is normally voluntary. More remarkable yet, if we excite a region situated between the occipital and temporal lobes we shall revive a memory of some kind, for instance a tune which he specially liked at one time and which he now "hears" again.

The scope for experiments on human beings is, obviously, very limited. Once again, recourse is had to animals—in particular, the cat. By trepanning under anesthesia, minute openings are made in the cranium and the animal is equipped with microelectrodes which cause it no discomfort, since the tissues of the cortex, which integrates sensations, are themselves insensible and cannot feel pain. The electrodes are connected by long leads to the apparatus, from which we can read the variations that the animal's activities cause in the patterns of the waves. We can, for example, watch the effect of a stimulus coming in from its receptors to the nervous center under observation, and we can see that the center responds to produce an action on the part of the cat.

If, on the other hand, we send a momentary but intense electric current along the wires connecting the recording apparatus to the electrodes, and in consequence to the cortical areas concerned, we actually *create behavior* in the animal: we can put it to sleep, make it thirsty or hungry, infuriate or soothe it, and so on. We can even invert its normal reactions, so that it responds by purring when its skin in pinched, or spits in response to stroking.

"A rat," says Dr. Chauchard, "will either kill a mouse or accept its presence, according to the state of its brain. Placing the electrodes in certain regions produces so pleasant an electrical stimulation that the rat will learn to stimulate itself by pressing a switch." And the same writer, reminding us that an ever more detailed *neuro-physiology of behavior* is being built up, adds: "Pavlov's refusal to be satisfied with a psychological explanation—the animal 'wants' or 'wills'—has led us to an understanding of what takes place physiologically when the animal wants or wills."

What is it that takes place during the establishment of a conditioned reflex—which, as we saw, depends on the association of a neutral stimulus (which then becomes conditional) with the absolute stimulus? Pavlov answers as follows:

"The basic condition for the formation of a conditioned reflex is a single or repeated coincidence in time of the arrival of a stimulus at a given point in the cortex, with the arrival of another, more intense stimulus at another point, which is also, in all likelihood, located in the cortex. At the end of a period of variable length, during which these coincidences are renewed, a smoother path is created between the two points; the connection is established."

And he proceeds to picture the cortex as a functional unity, "a grandiose mosaic" of responsive points—an essentially dynamic picture of the nervous system as it is displayed for us by modern methods of investigation.

THE CONDITIONED REFLEX IN NATURE

In nature, anything moving is a stimulus to an animal looking for food. All such stimuli act on the cortical structures; for example, they stimulate the retinas of the eyes, and the sensation is transmitted to the occipital areas by the optic nerve; they excite the eardrum, which acts on the chain of ossicles activating the cochlea, and the latter completes the transformation of the sound wave into a nervous impulse which travels along the acoustic nerve to its terminations in the temporal lobes. Above all, they excite the animal's olfactory sense. But none of these stimuli, until or unless it has become associated with the absolute stimulus "food," is "conditional." We repeat, the conditioned reflex is established only when two events coincide in time: the absolute stimulus, and a neutral stimulus acting on other sense organs. We are not forgetting that a conditional stimulus or a conditioned reflex can subsequently initiate new conditioned reflexes, but the source of conditioning is always instinct.

True, we are bound to admit the existence of a borderland which is hard to explore, a kind of no-man's-land between the innate and the acquired. Exactly where do innate reflexes end and conditioned reflexes begin? For instance, people say that a puppy sucks "instinctively," like the young of any other mammalian species, including man. But to what extent does maternal "instinct" intervene at birth to guide the puppy—in other words to initiate the first conditioned reflex, grafting it onto the absolute reflex (salivary and gastric secretion stimulated by contact with milk) and making the teats, and no other part of the dam's body, into a conditional stimulus?

Another example is the baby chick pecking the ground soon after hatching. But recent research enables us to say that the signal stimulus that causes it to do so is any small light-colored patch on the ground; only later, *by experience,* does it learn to distinguish between a grain of corn and a tiny pebble.

To return to the weaned puppy with which Pavlov experimented, and which had been parted from its mother but kept exclusively on a milk diet: it did not salivate at the *sight* of meat until after it had tasted meat for the first time. It undoubtedly did salivate on the first occasion when meat was put into its mouth, and we can therefore take it that the reflex of salivation at the taste of meat is an absolute reflex; what is not absolute is "psychical" salivation, provoked merely by the sight of meat—the meat becoming a conditional stimulus, acting at a distance, only after having been *recognized* as an object provoking secretion.

Conditions in the natural state are very different from those in the laboratory. The puppy comes into contact with meat long before weaning, since meat is his dam's food; there is no perceptible interim between the phenomenon of absolute and that of psychical salivation. But imagine the case of an experimental dog in a laboratory, which has never encountered meat and which happens to escape into natural conditions one day, at about the age of weaning. Will it ever taste meat or will it not? It is hungry; it wanders about, sniffing *instinctively*, like all its kind, and running after anything that moves—this being as firmly established an instinct as the innate reflex of investigation (which Pavlov sometimes picturesquely referred to as the reflex of "What is it?"); and—obeying another instinct, which can also be observed in babies—it puts all sorts of objects into its mouth, some of which, by an *innate reflex*, will cause salivation on coming into contact with the oral mucosa, leading either to the immediate ejection of the object or to its ingestion.

From now on, new conditioned reflexes will be set up in the dog as a result of the coincidence of conditional stimuli with the absolute stimulus. It will turn away from one substance and pounce on another, especially meat, which will be recognized not only by sight, but also and more particularly by smell. Other stimuli, in themselves completely neutral with respect to the alimentary reflex, will quickly come into action. A stray dog in a city makes for a closed, empty dustbin—a conditioned reflex arising from the fact that, *usually*, a dustbin contains food which can be reached by lifting the lid, an action which the dog must have performed quite fortuitously in the first place, scrabbling impatiently at the bin because of the attractive smells emanating from it. In a very short time the mere noise of somebody putting rubbish into the bin will be enough to make the dog come running up. And when it has found a friendly welcome at a butcher's shop, it quickly learns to distinguish that shop from others, where the same appetizing smells fill the air but the only presents given are kicks, which *inhibit the alimentary reflex.*

In woods or fields, on prairies or pampas, innumerable conditioned reflexes are created in like fashion in the wild animal. The twitter of a bird, the bleat of a wild sheep or goat, make the beast of prey crouch; and when bird or sheep or goat takes to flight, its movement triggers off the hunting animal's reflex of attack. Through conditioning, the carnivore learns not to put itself upwind of its prey, which its smell puts to flight, just as the smell of the prey is a conditional stimulus to the carnivore. And the grazing herbivore, alerted by the suspect cracking of a branch, flees just as readily from the sound as it would from the actual sight of the carnivore, and in so doing is once more obeying a conditioned reflex.

Old-fashioned books tell us that every wild animal "instinctively" runs away from man. This *a priori* judgment is just as arbitrary as can be. To quote an example first mentioned by Charles Darwin, that of the Galapagos Islands, none of the animals in the then unexplored archipelago took fright on seeing the new species of bipeds which had come to visit them.

Many writers have reported that, in various parts of the world, animals flee from man only when he is carrying a gun. It is true that this is not authenticated beyond all doubt; but if it was, it would be easy enough to explain: the conditional stimulus of the flight-reflex would be the "thing that goes bang and kills," not the creature handling it.

A few years ago, tender-hearted people were delighted to hear that a panther and a hen had settled down amicably together while being transported by air from a zoo in Europe to one in America; the hen had, of course, been put into the cage in case the panther felt hungry on the journey. But the cause of the idyll was probably the simple fact that the panther was seeing a hen for the first time in its life, so that no association had been built up in its cortex between this "object" and the experience of eating. And we shall probably not be far wrong in supposing that the hen was also having its first sight of a panther.

If things had been otherwise, if the hen had been confined with a kitten or a dog, for example, it would probably have panicked, flapped its wings and in general behaved in such a way that, *by reaction,* the panther, equally alarmed, would have put an end to the fuss with a blow of its paw; then, attracted by the smell of warm blood, in accordance with an innate reflex, it would have eaten its late companion. But as neither of the two animals was accustomed to regard the other as a stimulus of any kind, they got on excellently together. It was stated at the time that when they reached their destination the happy pair were reluctant to part. No doubt these reports were a little overdone; still, it might have been as well to leave the creatures together for the sake of the charming picture they made.

Cats and dogs are said to be "hereditary enemies." But it is well known that if they are brought up together, sharing the same games (all young animals are instinctively inclined to play), they never do each any harm. Cats, indeed, have been known to rear litters of mice with their kittens. Other examples lead us to believe that the very "hunting instinct" itself is a myth. What is real and fundamental is the innate reflex of alimentation and the innate reflex of investigation (both of which can be observed as low in the scale of life as the amoeba, in the form of continual movements with no precise goal); all other behavior is subsequently grafted onto these two by means of conditioning. It seems likely that humanity itself, in the early days of its development, was subject to this general rule.

And even if we had to admit the existence of a rudimentary hunting instinct it would still be possible to explain it by the transformation of certain conditioned reflexes, through successive generations, into innate reflexes. Pavlov believed in the possibility of this transition from genotype to phenotype, but it must be conceded that no convincing proof has ever been put forward. No definite assertion can be made about the matter, however sure we may be that a belief in evolution is incompatible with a denial that acquired characteristics can be inherited.

However that may be, the innate reflexes or instincts—however acutely they are developed in the higher species, and however adequate for vegetative functioning and the simplest essentials of the relationship between the inner and outer media—are clearly quite inadequate for normal existence under natural conditions, with all the freedom but also all the hazards which those conditions imply.

To sum up this section, here is a page from Pavlov which deals with human beings as well as animals:

"The most essential connection between the animal organism and the surrounding world is that brought about by certain chemical substances which constantly enter into the chemical composition of the given organism, i.e. the food connection. In the lower forms of the animal world it is the direct contact between food and the animal organism or vice versa, which chiefly leads to alimentary metabolism. In the higher forms these relations become more numerous and remote. Now odors, sounds and pictures attract the animals to food substances, already in wide regions of the surrounding world. And in the highest formation the sound of speech, as well as written and printed characters, send human beings all over the world in search of daily bread. Thus, numberless, diverse and distant external agents act, as it were, as food signals, directing the higher animals to acquire it and making them establish food connections with the external world. Along with this variety and remoteness, there takes place a substitution of the temporary for the constant connection between the external agents and the organism; first, because, essentially, the remote connections are of a temporary and changeable nature, and, secondly, because, due to their variety and number, they cannot be covered as constant connections, even by the most capacious apparatus. The given food object may be now in one place, now in another; it may, consequently, be accompanied at one time by certain phenomena, at another time by quite different ones; it may be part of one or another system of the external world, and therefore now these other natural phenomena must temporarily serve as stimulating agents producing in the organism a positive motor (in the broad sense of the word) reaction to this object."

CONDITIONED REFLEXES IN THE LABORATORY

It was not merely the chance fact of having made the digestive glands the object of his first studies which caused Pavlov to choose the mechanism of secretion as the foundation on which to build up a physiological theory of behavior.

By the method of permanent fistulas he was able to obtain precise quantitative measurements of the amount of secretions caused either by contact with food or by stimulation at a distance, and also to appreciate them qualitatively, by analysis. It is impossible to exaggerate the importance of this experimental precision.

"At first," he writes, "in our psychical experiments with the psychical glands . . . we conscientiously endeavored to explain our results by imagining the subjective state of the animal. But nothing came of this except sterile controversy and individual views that could not be reconciled. And so we could do nothing but conduct the research on a purely objective basis; our first and especially important task was completely to abandon the very natural tendency to transfer our own subjective state to the mechanism of the reaction of the animal undergoing the experiment and to concentrate instead on studying the correlation between the external phenomena and the reaction of the organism. . . . In the physiological case the activity of the salivary glands is connected with the properties of the substance on which the effect of the saliva is directed. The saliva moistens dry substances and any ingested material; it neutralizes the chemical effect of the substances.

These properties constitute the special stimuli of the specific mouth surface. Consequently, in the physiological experiments the animal is stimulated by the essential, unconditioned properties of the object in relation to the physiological role of the saliva.

"In the psychical experiments the animal is excited by the properties of the external object, which are inessential for the activity of salivary glands, or even entirely accidental. The visual, acoustic and even purely olfactory properties of our objects, when they are present in other objects, do not of themselves exert any influence on the salivary glands which, in their turn, so to speak, have no business relations with these properties.

"In the psychical experiments the salivary glands are stimulated not only by the properties of the objects inessential for the work of the glands, but absolutely by all the conditions surrounding these objects, or with which they are connected one way or another—for example, the dish in which they are contained, the article on which they are placed, the room, the people who usually bring the objects, even the noises produced by these people, though the latter may not be seen at the given moment—their voices, even the sound of their steps.

"Thus, in psychical experiments, the connection of the objects acting as stimuli on the salivary glands becomes more and more distant and delicate. Here, undoubtedly, we have a phenomenon of further adaptation. We can admit in this case that such a distant delicate connection as that between the step of the person who usually feeds the animal and the working of the salivary glands has no specific physiological significance other than its delicacy. But we need only recall those animals whose saliva contains protective poison, to appreciate the great vital significance of this timely provision of a protective means against an approaching enemy."

So many environmental factors are operative in the formation of a conditioned reflex that in order to make sure of obtaining precise observations Pavlov and his collaborators had to organize entirely new laboratory arrangements, which have remained models of their kind ever since. The chief feature was double cubicles, separated by a partition. In one cubicle was a stand on which the experimental animal was placed, usually a dog with fistulas of the kind already described. It was kept in position by a harness preventing free movement. As will be remembered, the fistulas were provided with funnels for collecting the secretions. These funnels were connected by flexible tubing to graduated test tubes in the adjacent cubicle.

The latter was occupied by the experimenter, sitting at his work table, conveniently placed to watch and measure the quantities of juice secreted (the juices being later analyzed). The experimenter also had charge of the controls directing distant stimuli.

In front of the animal a movable shelf was so arranged that food could be presented when required. An electric bulb could be shone before its eyes; a bell could be rung and a metronome could be set beating; a scented vapor (usually aniseed essence) could be released; and so on.

But, despite all these precautions, a number of disturbances from the outside world interfered all too frequently with the conduct of experiments. Pavlov therefore, in 1910, asked for a special building to be erected—the famous "Tower of Silence," which, however, was not put up until after the advent of the Soviets.

The "Tower of Silence," designed in accordance with Pavlov's requirements, consists of three stories. The first and third stories provide working accommodation: eight rooms in all, with stalls for the animals. The intermediate story, low-ceilinged, contains laboratory apparatus. The windows are small, each glazed with a single sheet of thick plate glass (the lighting in the laboratories is of course provided by electricity and is uniform in quality); these windows keep out drafts, extremes of heat and cold, and smells and noise. The floors are supported on steel girders whose ends are bedded in sand to eliminate vibration. All the doors are double, made of steel, and close hermetically. Round the base of the tower runs a moat filled with straw.

We repeat, secretion was selected by Pavlov as the basis of his experiments on conditioned reflexes only because it offered scope for consistent verification of the commonest of such reflexes, and the precise quantitative and qualitative evaluation of the stimuli employed. Secretion provided the test without which the theory could not have been established. But one must completely abandon any idea that secretion is essential to the study of reflexes as a whole.

One of the usual ways of training a dog to give you its paw is to offer it a titbit, say a lump of sugar, and to take the paw in your hand and raise it, with the command, "Give me your paw!" or simply, "Paw!" The absolute stimulus is the sugar, the conditional stimulus the sound of your voice.

After a few repetitions, during which the absolute and conditional stimuli are employed simultaneously, it becomes possible to elicit the conditioned reflex—lifting the paw—by means of the conditional stimulus alone (the voice uttering the words, "Give me your paw!" or the one word, "Paw!").

Of course the natural tendency is to say the dog has "understood" that he is to give his paw. This is untrue; or at least, this subjective, psychological interpretation does not genuinely account for what has happened. If we had conducted our experiment with full scientific rigor, using a dog whose secretions could be collected by means of a fistula, we would have seen that the dog *salivated on hearing the spoken command.*

Unfortunately, it is also true, as is shown by the unlovely example of animal trainers who employ cruelty, that the reflex could equally well have been obtained by means not of an alimentary but a painful stimulus: blows, electric shocks, pinching, or the like. In this event the reflex action clearly proceeds from inhibition, a phenomenon we shall have more to say about later; all we want to convey here is that secretion is not indispensable as the precondition for the formation of a conditioned reflex: the dog will give its paw in order to *stop the pain,* this being the absolute stimulus with which the conditional stimulus, the sound of the voice, is associated. As in the previous case a few repetitions, in which the conditional and the absolute stimulus are brought to bear simultaneously, establish the conditioned reflex, and the dog offers his paw whenever he hears the command, "Paw!"

THE MAIN PRECONDITIONS

Pavlov indicates, as the main precondition for the formation of a conditioned reflex, *the combination of an indifferent (i.e. neutral) stimulus and an unconditioned (i.e. innate) reflex.* He emphasizes, however, that if a new conditioned reflex is to be quickly established and firmly consolidated, the new (conditional) stimulus must be much weaker than the unconditional stimulus, and must slightly precede it in point of time. It is also important that during the period when the conditioned reflex is being built up, the brain should be in good functional health and that the subject's general health should also be satisfactory.

A multitude of internal and external factors are capable

of throwing the experiment out of gear. For example, if a dog has already been feasting on sweets it will be difficult to make him give his paw by offering him a lump of sugar, when he has been getting plenty of sugar beforehand, unconditionally. A fully-fed animal turns away from food; what hope is there of setting up a salivary conditioned reflex by means of an indifferent stimulus when the absolute stimulus no longer provokes the secretory reflex?

Again, a conditioned reflex that has been satisfactorily established will fade out if we consistently use the conditional reflex alone. If we try to get a dog to give its paw at the word of command only, without occasionally adding the reward of a lump of sugar (absolute stimulus), the moment will come when the conditioned reflex no longer operates. But we must emphasize that there is no question of the reflex being totally and permanently obliterated. Pavlov stressed the fact (and his prolonged and detailed researches gave him the authority to do so) that "the conditioned reflex does not disappear without trace." There is no question, according to him, of "a destruction of the temporary connection," but only of its "more or less complete and persistent functional blocking, by inhibition."

The question of inhibition in higher nervous activity is so important as to demand a section to itself. But we must pass it over for the moment in favor of another problem: the *irradiation* and *concentration* of excitation, as described by Pavlov; pointing out at the same time that his conception is under dispute at the present day.

IRRADIATION AND CONCENTRATION OF EXCITATIONS

Pavlov showed that conditional stimuli participate in the building of a new conditioned reflex only by virtue of their most general properties: a conditioned reflex reaction to sound, for example, can be elicited by notes lower or higher in pitch than that used in the conditioning process. The same observation holds good for conditional stimuli affecting other senses besides sound—sight, smell, and touch in all its forms.

Sensory messages, picked up by the specialized organs and traveling along the afferent nerves to the centers in which they are received, translated and re-transmitted, undeniably make their way to the hemispheres—since, as we have seen, the visual (occipital lobes), the olfactory (rhinencephalon) and the tactile (parietal lobes).

Stimulation reaching the hemispheres is *irradiated.* In the words of Pavlov, who regarded this as the *first law of stimulation*: "It is immediately generalized." He put forward the following example: "If the sound of a metronome becomes the conditional stimulus of secretion from the salivary glands, other noises which one may employ will, *at first*, also provoke secretion."

We have italicized "at first" to emphasize the provisional nature of this observation.

"The processes of excitation and inhibition," * Pavlov states, "as soon as they have developed in the hemispheres, are irradiated without delay."

Here are two experiments in conditioning which show that the irradiation of excitation, as it occurs in a conditioned reflex, is far from being a figment of the imagination: "If," writes Pavlov, "a note of 1,000 vibrations a second is converted into a conditional stimulus, and if we subsequently try other sounds, even though widely different in pitch, we find that they produce the same reaction. It is the same with other stimuli; if, by the usual method, pricking the same part of the skin on a number of occasions is turned into a conditional stimulus, a salivary secretion is obtained; and when we subsequently try pricking other parts of the skin we also obtain a certain quantity of saliva, thus proving that excitation has been propagated in the hemispheres and that all areas of the cortical region now react in the same way as that concerned in the original stimulus."

But as a sequel to the law of irradiation of excitation Pavlov discovered another law, which he named the law of *concentration of excitation.*

This law, like the other, was derived from observation and was confirmed by numerous experiments: "Suppose we obtain from a dog a conditioned reaction to a metronome, and that we provoke the reflex several times in succession. We shall see that other sounds gradually cease to be effective, and that a moment comes when only the metronome has the power of provoking the conditioned reflex. This concentration of excitation can even proceed further: if we continue to elicit the reaction with the metronome" (meanwhile, of course, continuing to reinforce it with the absolute stimu-

* We shall see later that inhibition itself is essentially a process of excitation.

lus—*author's note*), "we shall soon find that only the particular tempo which we have been using will elicit a reaction when the conditional response alone is sought" (i.e. when the absolute stimulus is not also present). "Discrimination in such cases reaches a considerable degree of refinement; for instance, the dog will react to a tempo of 100 beats a minute but will remain indifferent to 96. Physiologically, the totality of the hemispheric zone irradiated, in area and depth, has been spatially reduced, that is to say that the nervous influx produced by the stimulus is now communicated only to a very limited area of the cortical zone under consideration."

Here is a still more precise indication. A dog has been conditioned to salivate in response to a tactile stimulus, a slight prick at a certain place on the skin. In the early period of the functioning of the conditioned reflex (with the conditional stimulus, the prick, being used by itself) the dog will react to any other tactile stimulus as well, applied to any part of the skin. But suppose we prolong the conditioning process, choosing always the same small and carefully defined area of the skin for pricking, and presenting the absolute stimulus (food) a few moments later. At other times during the process, pricking is effected in other parts of the skin but food is not offered; and these supplementary prickings are progressively brought closer and closer to the chosen area. When we return to the conditioned reflex, which has by now been thoroughly established, and apply only the conditional stimulus (pricking), we shall find that the animal no longer salivates except when the stimulus is applied to just that area with which the presence of the absolute stimulus was associated. This site of conditional stimulation of the skin, which has become spatially much reduced, is matched by a similarly reduced irradiation in the cerebral hemisphere.

This example sets an important problem: that of the transformation of a reflex of pain, however slight, provoked by pricking, into a salivary reflex, which is at least to some extent a manifestation of enjoyment.

No one before Pavlov had tried to explain paradoxical reactions of this kind, though they are by no means rare either in animals or in man. Indeed, they occur much more prominently in our own species, notably in the form of the disquieting masochism sometimes found associated with the sexual instinct. We shall come back to this problem; meanwhile, let us see what is meant by inhibition.

INHIBITION

Inhibition is simply an excitation that works antagonistically to other excitations and their effects, so that they are prevented from arising at all, or else are delayed or slowed down or even halted in mid-career. In this sense and this sense only, it is possible to speak of negative reflexes, as distinct from positive reflexes. This means that inhibition is in no way a passive process, and though its end result is sometimes a state of inertia or stupor, its origin lies in an excitation involving energy expenditure.

How could it be otherwise, life being essentially a dynamic process? Inhibition can be observed at the cellular level; to be precise, at neuronic level. The cell never exhibits the completely passive state of rest found in machines, which in the case of the cell would mean death (we shall see in a later section that sleep itself depends on an excitation which causes a process of inhibition).

Only three states are possible for the neuron: *(a)* normal functioning, consisting of metabolism throughout the neuron and polarization on its surface; *(b)* the state of excitement; *(c)* the state of inhibition.

The state of excitation means that the neuron is *reacting*: receiving messages centripetally, responding to them centrifugally. It is never a passive conductor: to every sensation it responds with a pulsation in response.

The state of inhibition means that the neuron has *disconnected itself*: it is no longer receiving messages and in consequence no longer supplying responses, or at least its reactions are decelerated, impeded, by a process which is the reverse of passive; it is defending itself against excitation and in order to do so must make an expenditure of energy, in the form of a heightened polarization of its own surface.

"The neuron," as Dr. Chauchard explains, "thus displays a fluctuating activity which oscillates about the mean state of basic vital activity: between excitation on the one hand (active work, orientated externally, i.e. to the receiving and sending of messages, and causing fatigue) and inhibition on the other hand (active braking, shutting the cell off from what is external to it)."

To give a drastically oversimplified picture of inhibition in the organism as a whole: I am about to cross a street because an interesting incident has excited my visual apparatus and touched off the reflex of walking (a muscular release; the reflex is absolutely positive). Suddenly, however, I see a car coming at full speed. I have a long-established conditioned reflex which prevents me from placing myself in the path of these diabolical machines, and my release into muscular activity is instantly arrested.

It is crystally clear that the reason for my remaining rooted to the curb was no mere "phenomenon of inertia," or whatnot, but *the result of a stimulus* which required a certain expenditure of energy in order to block my previous reflex (it is in this sense that we can talk of a negative reflex).

Pavlov gave convincing experimental proof of the reality of such inhibitory processes in cases where most of us would be content to assume, without further thought, that there was simply an absence of response. We have just seen how a conditioned reflex to sound was established, and how the concentration of irradiation was made evident by eliciting a delicate differentiation of the conditioning element: the particular metronome rhythm selected as the conditional stimulus was reinforced by the absolute stimulus (food), while other rhythms were left to do their work without this reinforcement. To put it more specifically, let us suppose that a conditioned reflex has been established in a dog by repeated applications of the stimuli, until the zone of irradiation has been limited in such a way that the reflex acts only at (say) 1,000 cycles a second, though at the beginning of the experiment any sound was capable of eliciting reflex action; now, at 10 cycles above or below 1,000, the dog no longer salivates. Have these frequencies become "indifferent"? No, answers Pavlov: "Instead of a positive effect they have acquired an inhibitory effect: they cause an inhibitory process in the central nervous system, and this can be quite easily proved. You try a note of 1,000 cycles per second; as before, it evokes a positive reflex, an alimentary reaction. You then employ one of the notes which have become ineffective, and immediately afterward you once again try the note of 1,000 cycles: *it will have temporarily lost its effect.* It follows that the other note must have created in the central nervous system an inhibition which takes a certain time to disappear."

We are led to observe not only the inhibitory effect itself, but also the fact that the inhibitory process is irradiated in exactly the same way as the excitatory. And there is nothing surprising in this; we know that they are ultimately identical in their nature.

We are also bound to concede that the irradiation of inhibition is progressively narrowed down; like the irradiation of excitation, it is subject to the law of concentration. As Pavlov said: "The oftener the unreinforced notes are used, the more restricted does irradiation of inhibition become: the process of inhibition becomes more and more concentrated in time and space."

There is obviously a wide variety of inhibitory processes: differential inhibition, as in the case just described, inhibition retarding a reflex, inhibition extinguishing a reflex, and so on. The simplest form of inhibition is that resulting from the preponderance of one reflex over another. To take a particularly simple example, a dog seizes a piece of meat, and, of course, salivates; at this precise moment it is given a violent blow with a whip, and salivation ceases instantaneously. Pavlov used the term "external inhibition" for this direct inhibitory process. The pain reflex is so powerful that it submerges the alimentary reflex.

Naturally, after a few such experiences and perhaps even only one, the mere sight of the whip is enough to elicit an inhibitory conditioned reflex; the dog stops salivating and no longer pounces on the meat. But all sorts of other stimuli, previously indifferent, will be equally effective in producing inhibition provided they have been associated with the use of the whip: such as the sight of the meat-safe from which it "stole" the meat or the table from which it took it; the plates and cutlery, the conversation of guests at the meal, and so on.

TRANSPOSITION OF EXCITATION

As we saw at the end of the last section but one, there are cases in which the significance of a painful stimulus is found to have been completely transformed.

Here is a hungry dog. We have arranged electrodes so as to be able to send him a powerful electric current, say in the thigh; then, almost simultaneously, we offer him meat; our intention, obviously, being to cause a salivary conditional reflex. At the first trial all we get is a defensive reaction on the animal's part. It is indeed likely that he will attack and try to bite us if he is irascible by nature, or if he is timid, that he will try to run away; but we shall not collect a single drop of saliva.

But the dog is really hungry. We tether him on the laboratory table, start giving him skin burns again, holding him firmly, and insinuate a piece of meat into his mouth, if necessary by force. He bites on it and salivates. After a few repetitions the dog will have quieted down, will put up with the burns, devour the meat, and will soon salivate abundantly with every manifestation of pleasure at the application of the electrodes, without meat.

Dr. Drabovitch, one of Pavlov's pupils, relates that Sherrington, after watching this experiment, cried in admiration, "At last I understand the psychology of the martyrs!"

The famous British scientist meant that the Christians, having been conditioned in advance to regard death as their means of liberation from "the evils of this world," and, moreover, being endowed by their faith with the "certainty" of eternal bliss, found their natural reflex of fear totally inhibited by the "promise" of life hereafter.

There can hardly be any doubt that some perversions, at least some cases of fetishism and masochism, are simply conditioned reflexes created under strong sexual excitement. It is by no means certain that orgasm itself is not a pain transformed into pleasure on the basis of an absolute reflex, the instinct of reproduction; for on examining the matter attentively one sees that the stimulation of the mucosae, followed by a loss of substance, "ought," logically, to be painful.

But we must abandon this interesting digression—which would in any case entail refuting the notion that the cortex plays the supreme role in the forming of conditioned reflexes; present-day knowledge makes it necessary to admit that more primordial structures are also involved. Let us hold to the main fact—namely, that conditioned reflexes, positive or negative, can be set up by means of any stimuli, provided these stimuli are registered by sensory receptors connected with integrating zones in the cortex, To quote Pavlov: "The conditional reflex is formed on the basis of all unconditional reflexes and from various agents of the internal medium and external environment both in their simplest and most complex forms, but with one limitation: it is formed only from those agents for the reception of which there are receptor elements in the cerebral hemispheres. Thus we have before us a very extensive synthesizing activity effected by this part of the brain."

EXCITATIONS, INHIBITIONS AND DYNAMIC STEREOTYPES

In the waking state, the brain is invaded by waves of stimulation and waves of inhibition between which there is continual reciprocal interference. This brings about a fluctuating and, in theory at any rate, harmonious activity of organisms in contact with their environment and interacting with other organisms of the same species or different species, with which they maintain various relationships. Very nearly all of our behavior consists of innate reflexes and conditioned reflexes. It is beyond doubt that many of our thoughts—if not all—are, or at least originate in, reflexes acquired from upbringing, education and culture, and strengthened by experience. Our thinking does not take place in, or start from, a vacuum. Perhaps intuition itself merely consists of memories which have been subjected to a delicate process of analysis and synthesis in the unconscious before emerging into consciousness. We say "perhaps," and no more.

In any case, pure thought is manifested as an activity of the cortical centers. "If we could see through the cranium," said Pavlov, "and if the zone of optimum excitability was luminous, we should see, in a man who was thinking, this supposedly luminous point of optimum excitability perpetually moving about. We could watch it continuously changing in shape and size. It would be surrounded by a zone of more or less dense shadow occupying the remainder of the hemispheres."

Pavlov held a very modern view of the brain's activity, similar to the picture now available to us as a result of electroencephalography and electrocorticography, both of which had only just begun to develop at the time of his death. At that juncture no one had assessed the wide implications of his discoveries; nor was Berger taken very seriously. Grey Walter brings out the situation clearly: "[The period from 1928 to 1935] was one of general skepticism, neglect of Berger's original observations, undervaluation of Pavlov's exploration, disregard of any possible connection between them. The technical devices of the period were so poor, and Berger's data were so poorly presented, that this cannot be regarded as surprising."

Pavlov drew the following picture: "Countless stimuli, different in nature and intensity, reach the cerebral hemispheres both from the external world and the internal medium of the organism itself. Whereas some of them are merely investigated (the orienting reflex), others evoke highly diverse conditioned and unconditioned effects. They all meet, come together, interact, and they must, finally, become systematized, equilibrated, and form, so to speak, a *dynamic stereotype*."

British researchers have chosen the name *pattern* for the dynamic stereotype. Another expression is *spatio-temporal schemata*; that is, fluctuating physiological structures consisting of excitations and inhibitions, and associating or separating the cerebral neurons in terms of time and space.

Underlying all cerebral activity is the work of 14 billion neurons, with their unending cycle of vital energy. These neurons are in a state of preparedness to receive messages from without or within the organisms through the channels of the senses. By their interference with one another these messages create new circuits; or much more frequently, in the adult, cause existing schemata to reassert themselves and spread through the cortex—which then by its own internal activity and in a reflex fashion (making use of both innate and acquired reactions, one reflex eliciting another, positive or negative, and so on, in long and complicated sequences) initiates motor reactions, which may not merely be a movement from place to place or some gesture of the hands but may equally well take the form of speech or writing.

At what point does pure thought, creative thought, appear in this process?

We do, after all, know that at certain moments we block, in some sort, *and in a definitely voluntary way*, the building of a sequence of patterns; we try to fix or stabilize them, as a preparation is "fixed" before being put under the microscope. We turn inward upon ourselves, we concentrate; we try to insulate our senses from the external world and if possible from the internal world as well; we become disconnected from the scheme of things and from ourselves. Noises, smells, changes of light, no longer impinge on us, and if we are unhappy at the time, our unhappiness momentarily disappears.

It seems to us as if only one thing was *working*—namely, our brain. And yet, if we are candid with ourselves, can we say that it was ever more thronged with "patterns" than at this moment? Is there some entity which creates thought—or is it created by us ourselves, that is to say by this conglomerate of cells which continues to live its physiological life even while striving to fashion something *absolutely* underived, *absolutely* new?

Now suppose we do manage to elaborate something unheard of, something never seen before; it will be built up of *absolutely* nothing but our previously existing patterns; no amount of argument will alter this fact. I would like the reader to try the experiment—as I did myself, before writing these few lines of which I have resolved to alter not a word.

HOW STEREOTYPES ARE UTILIZED

Starting out from the notion of dynamic stereotypes, Pavlov attempted to serve psychology by effecting a fruitful synthesis of two major trends in psychological thinking, the opposition between which had become apparent to him when he attended an international congress in the United States, in 1929. The contending parties were associationism and *Gestalt* psychology.

Associationism, which is purely mechanistic and empirical, regards all psychological phenomena as being no more than purely automatic associations of ideas; these associations themselves are supposed to have arisen through the combining of elements which were previously separate. Gestalt psychology, on the other hand, rejects every kind of "atomism." The psychologists of "form" (German *Gestalt*) regard psychical activity as being always a totality, and the psychologist's task as consisting of describing and interpreting *structures* of behavior (human or animal).

"The physiology of the cerebral hemispheres," says Pavlov, "makes it possible for us to unite these two points of view while basing ourselves on strictly experimental data. Here is one of the very simple facts which illustrate this: establish a series of conditioned reflexes to various stimuli by bringing them to bear in a fixed order and at equal intervals; if you then change the intervals or the order of the stimuli you will obtain quite different effects. The process of forming the system plays such an important role that cases are not rare in which this change of order makes all the conditioned reflexes disappear. Therefore, from our point of view, the cortex carries out both the work of analysis and that of synthesis. Every *opposition* from one kind of work toward the other, every *preference* given to one or the other in the course of research, will preclude lasting success and will prevent the building-up of an adequate picture of cerebral activity. Just as, in the hands of the chemist, analysis and synthesis are powerful means with which to study the structure of some unknown compound, so also for the physiologist the analysis and synthesis of the nervous processes offer a sure road to the comprehension of the highly complex structure of human cerebral functioning."

It is quite clear that, basically, the functioning of the nervous system is a matter of pure physiology and is hence a part of the whole system of biology, which depends entirely on metabolic exchanges having their roots deep in physiochemical determinism. The organism's normal functioning takes place through the automatic functioning of cells and, on a larger structural scale, of organs (the automatism of the heart is the most striking example). The regulation of these automatic activities depends on the vegetative nervous system, either directly, or indirectly through hormonal mediation and with the aid of innumerable feedback phenomena.

This grandiose structure is erected in gradual stages, starting with the union of the two parental gametes, passing through the various phases of embryonic development, and determined by the chromosomes present in the gametes, which convey the characteristics that the individual inherits, and which are the result of the slow evolution of life and species in a natural environment, in the course of something between 2 and 3 billion years. An evolution at once complex and complexifying, whose mechanism we are far from understanding as yet, but whose results can on the whole be explained in terms of biological laws.

Next, in addition to the various material exchanges between the inner and outer media, the individual makes contact with the external world from the moment his extra-uterine existence begins; a contact effected in terms of the innate reflexes which form part of his hereditary patrimony. Here again we are undoubtedly faced with automatism; and the law of cause and effect is in no way nullified by the fact that we spend most of our time registering the effects of causes of which the greater part as yet escapes us. We tend to think what Pavlov in fact believed, that the innate reflexes are acquired reflexes which have gradually become ingrained in the various species, while at the same time summations were being transformed into mutations by environmental influences; but the possibility of such changes is far from having been proved, and we cannot dogmatize about it.

With only its instincts to guide it the animal cannot successfully confront new situations. But we have seen that even unicellular animals, endowed merely with tropisms, are capable of some variety in behavior (though the scope of this variety is very limited in time and space). Hence it looks as if the cell itself were capable of receiving impressions, in some sense; which means that stimuli from the external world apparently elicit new, different reactions by tracing out new paths, the schemata for which would be provided by memory traces superimposed more or less sporadically, as circumstances might determine, on the pre-existing schema.

It is incontrovertible that the capacity for new acquisitions becomes greater as we ascend the evolutionary ladder—in other words, as we come to species having a more highly developed nervous organization. Conditioning becomes progressively more efficient as cortical elements are added to the earlier components. We have seen that conditioned reflexes can be set up in species not endowed with an encephalon, but that the possession of cerebral hemispheres permits the elaboration of a number of such reflexes, a number which becomes impressively greater as the hemispheres increase in size and in the complexity of their convolutions.

In the higher species, it looks very much as if the innate reflexes were located in the subcortical layers; as, indeed, they are in the less highly evolved species, in whose case also these reflexes represent spatio-temporal schemata, the subtle mechanism of which is called into play by internal or external sensory stimuli.

Pavlov writes: "The organism accomplishes, among the objects and influences of the environment, the special actions necessary for maintaining the integrity both of the organism and of its species. These actions are the alimentary, defense, and sexual reactions, and others, some of which are secretory. These special actions—movements and secretions—are effected in a complete synthesis of the organisms's internal activity; in other words, the activity of the internal organs must correspond to the realization of motor activity. They are stimulated in accordance with a stereotype, by a few, definite, internal and external stimuli. We call them 'most complex special unconditioned reflexes' " (in order to distinguish them from the absolute unconditioned reflexes—*author's note*). "Others give them different names: instinct, tendencies, dispositions, etc. Anatomically, these activities depend on the subcortical nodes near the cortex."

We have seen that surgical removal of the cortex, for instance in the dog, does not prevent this basic activity, and that Pavlov had good reason to affirm—as later research has confirmed—that the cortex is not required for instinctive activities (unconditioned, innate activities, whether absolute or complex). This is not at all the same thing as saying that in day-to-day existence the cortex plays no part in instinctive movements; but just that, in ordinary circumstances, the interplay of unconditioned and conditioned reflexes becomes extremely subtle, with a complexity that is beyond experimental observation. What we must remember is, for example, that the decerebrate dog cannot even feed itself unaided. It will masticate mechanically if its nose is thrust into its bowl; otherwise it will stand in front of the bowl without feeding, although its optical apparatus is intact; it can "see," but it cannot translate the image; it lacks the centers by which visual images are integrated.

As Pavlov says: "The special unconditioned reflexes constitute the essential basis of the animal's external activity. But in the higher animals, if nothing is added to these activities—if they alone are present—the instincts are clearly inadequate to preserve the individual and the race. The decorticate dog, if left to itself, soon dies, without exception. For the preservation of the individual and the species it is absolutely necessary that the work of the lower brain-structures be supplemented by another instrument, the cerebral hemispheres. These perform an analysis and synthesis of the external world, distinguishing or combining its isolated elements. Out of these elements and their combinations the cortical apparatus makes innumerable signals which orientate and regulate the activity of the subcortical structures. Thus these structures are enabled to adjust their activities to external conditions with delicacy and precision."

So far the whole process is mechanical. It is in a purely deterministic way that the animal develops conditioned reflexes of the kind which we have seen being created in the laboratory, and which the impact of innumerable stimuli elicits from moment to moment during its life in the natural state.

The unconditioned reflexes, on the other hand, work from the inside outward, impelling the animal to satisfy various functions over and above those comprised by the vegetative system (which is the unconditioned realm *par excellence*): the alimentary reflex, reflexes of aggression, freedom, play, investigation ("What is it?"), sexuality, maternity, and so on. "Consider, for example," says Pavlov, "the special unconditioned alimentary reflex, consisting of movements toward the external substance on which the animal feeds, of ingestion into the digestive tract, and of the secretion of juices. We do not know exactly what stimulus sets off this reflex in the first place; we know only that a few hours after a meal even a decorticate dog will emerge from its intermittent sleep and begin to walk about, to wander restlessly."

We say, "The dog is hungry," and force its nose into its bowl; and as soon as it is satisfied it falls asleep again. But this decorticate dog would, as we have said, be quite capable of dying of hunger in the presence of a full feeding-bowl, because it has been deprived of the power to integrate conditional stimuli.

The decerebrate dog, says Pavlov, undoubtedly shows an alimentary impulse, but the movement is vague and does not reach its objective. "If, while walking about, the animal salivated, that was not the result of a stimulus from the external world but only of an internal stimulus."

Now consider the behavior of a dog with its brain intact, in similar conditions; that is, some time after having eaten he is once again "hungry" (an internal stimulus registered at subcortical level). He has woken up and his senses are alert; if he catches sight of his bowl the conditioned reflex will come into action. He displays not only physiological salivation; it is psychical as well. But suppose the bowl is empty: he will sniff about for food elsewhere. In nature, this is the moment at which the carnivorous animal "goes hunting." A number of conditional stimuli—noises, smells, movements, etc., will guide him toward anything that might be suitable as prey. He will lurk in ambush, conditioned as he is to wait, crouching, and then patiently stalk his elusive, grazing victim. Pavlov remarked that in this case an inhibitory reflex arrested salivary secretion. The whole of this sketch is valid, *mutatis mutandis*, for every phase of behavior, with all its interactions both active and passive between the previously established spatio-temporal schemata, innate and acquired.

In man, whose instincts are underdeveloped compared with those of animals, conditioned reflexes govern nearly the whole of behavior. The mechanism of conditioning, broadly speaking, is the same as in animals; but in the form of speech (and writing, which is an extension of speech) man possesses what Pavlov called a *second signal system.*

THE SECOND SIGNAL SYSTEM

We can immediately grasp what Pavlov meant by *"the second signal system"* by means of a very simple example, the salivary conditioned reflex, which, as the expression "mouth-watering" implies, has been known for centuries and centuries, though it was only recently recognized as a conditioned reflex. Physical salivation in man occurs in exactly the same way as it does in dogs in Pavlov's classical experiments: a conditional stimulus of any kind, having been associated with the absolute stimulus (food), will subsequently evoke, when applied alone, the same reaction as the absolute stimulus would have caused in the given conditions.

"In the given conditions" means that, just as we would have had no urge to eat some dish or other, however appetizing, if it was offered when we had already eaten our fill, so also shall we not salivate at the sight or mention of the said dish and the conditional stimuli associated with it, if for any reason (such as being ill or having recently fed) we are not in a state to consume it. It is in fact very obvious, and a matter of current observation, that while we may be caused to salivate by the smells emanating from a cheap eating-house which we pass on our way to lunch, we may be repelled on the way back by those wafted from a luxury restaurant.

With Pavlov, we regard any conditional stimulus or group of conditional stimuli which are capable of engendering a conditioned reflex (as, for example, salivation, in an alimentary context), as being "primary signals." But, with the use of speech and the capacity of conceptual thought which speech brings with it, man possesses an instrument by means of which he can describe all the phenomena surrounding him, that is to say all the impressions made on him by the sensory stimuli which come to him from the various environments in which he moves.

The word—the basic element of language, whether spoken or written—is an abstraction by means of which any phenomenon or group of phenomena can be described. Words can therefore act as a conditional stimulus, in conjunction with either the absolute stimulus itself or other conditional stimulus, to activate a conditioned reflex: if to a hungry man we say "bread" or "stew," or describe a gargantuan meal, his mouth will water—he will salivate, as Pavlov's dogs did.

Note that we can equally well condition a dog to salivate at the word "meat," for example; but in this case something quite different is going on. The specific sound is what brings on the conditioned reflex action in the animal, just as the dinner bell at a boardinghouse makes a guest salivate when he is returning hungry from a long walk; a conditional stimulus consisting merely of an emission of sound waves. Later, the mere word "bell," despite its never having been associated with the absolute stimulus (the meal), may be enough to make our mouths water if we are in a sufficiently receptive state.

Another example: a little child picks up a fruit he has never seen before, a yellow fruit, pointed at both ends; if he bites this fruit (a lemon) its acidity will make him salivate copiously, and it is perfectly certain that he will thereafter salivate every time he sees a lemon, even without tasting it. But he will not salivate at all on hearing the spoken word *"lemon," unless someone has shown or explained to him, or he has happened to discover for himself, that the yellow, highly acid fruit is called a "lemon."*

Pavlov's exposition is as follows: "If our sensations and ideas of the world about us are, for us, the *primary signals* of reality—concrete signals—speech, and especially the kinesthetic stimuli which pass from the speech organs to the cortex, are *secondary signals*, 'signals of signals.' They represent an abstraction from reality; it is precisely they which constitute our superior and specifically human intelligence. Speech is a real conditional stimulus to human beings, as real as the others, which are common to animals as well; but this one stimulus is far more inclusive than any other. In this respect there is no comparison, qualitative or quantative, between speech and the conditional stimuli of animals."

We have chosen alimentary examples for our illustrations here because they can be easily verified by observing psychical secretions, which take place independently of the will; but the same process can easily be found taking place anywhere else in our activities. Moreover, the role of the spoken word can also be played by the written. It is undeniable that our mouths water not only when we hear the word "lemon," but also when we read it. But we shall also salivate at the mere *thought* of a lemon (mentally evoking either a visual image or the word)—a fact which enables us to understand that many phenomena of thought depend simply on conditioning.

Let us look at this more closely.

Upbringing is conditioning pure and simple. A newborn baby possesses innate reflexes which are specific to human kind, just as the young of any other animal displays instincts proper to its own species. It must be admitted that the baby is at a clear disadvantage where instinct is concerned; other young animals are much better endowed. If we make an impartial comparison between a puppy and a baby we shall see that the former gets on to level terms with life much sooner. If an observer from another planet, knowing nothing of the laws of life on earth, were to watch the development of a puppy and a baby that were born at the same time, without taking any account of the parents and their activities, he would jump to the premature conclusion that of these two little quadrupeds the furry one was easily the more intelligent.

A few years before the war two American animal psychologists, Mr. and Mrs. Kellog, performed an unusual experiment. They reared their son Donald, aged ten months at the start of the experiment, and a female chimpanzee, Gua, aged seven and a half months, together *and in identical conditions*. Donald and Gua were looked after in exactly the same way: they had the same games, went for the same little outings, slept in similar beds; in short, their upbringing was the same.

Generally speaking, Gua was far more precocious than Donald. She was the first to learn how to use a spoon. It was not she who imitated the child, but the child who imitated her; this applied specially to her practice of gnawing at furniture and the like.

Gua was much quicker to respond to commands from their "parents." But when, through conditioning, Donald had learned not only to understand human, conceptual language, but also to speak it, he drew ahead rapidly, whereas Gua had reached her "ceiling."

MAN THE SLOW DEVELOPER

The human fetus, as we know from the example of premature babies, is capable of living in the outside world from the seventh month of pregnancy. But although the general structure of its cortex is complete, the full anatomical development of the cortex is not. The fact that a child cannot stand up at birth, as a foal can, is caused not by any muscular deficiency or by immaturity of the medullary structures, through which, by an innate reflex, the action of walking is controlled; the cause is immaturity of the pyramidal cells of the cortex, whose processes run down into the centers of the medulla, the activities of which they control.

The psychological backwardness of the human young is the result of physiological backwardness. A child, in the earliest stages, shows far less aptitude than a young animal for acquiring conditioned reflexes. Thus, whereas a monkey is adult at from five to eight years, the anatomical development of the human brain is incomplete until the age of seven or thereabouts, and his cortex, like the rest of his body, goes on developing for some time after that. The encephalogram of a human being does not become "normal" until about the age of eighteen years.*

A child babbles, without apparent meaning, because of an innate reflex. This is the stage at which to set up a conditioned reflex, grafting on to this emission of *sounds* (which are comparable to those emitted by animals) the rudiments of conceptual language. It is worth knowing that the aptitude for this primordial apprenticeship is expendable; it disappears if it is not used. A baby left to itself till the age of five will be difficult to train. A child's brain is a frail, malleable instrument which must without fail be made to func-

* Of course this is only the average. It is quite possible that in some individuals, cortical development is accelerated by factors as yet unknown (this would be the case with child prodigies), while in others it is retarded (this might be the case with late learners, self-taught people).

tion; otherwise it becomes rigid beyond hope of recall. This is why a child's earliest environment is of such vast importance. If the adults of primitive peoples are incapable of rising to a certain cultural level it is not because of any "hereditary disability" but because, at the stage when the brain is undergoing the most important part of its physiological growth, they happen to be in a primitive environment, a society which can offer them nothing more than it possesses itself. This factor—often aggravated by nutritional deficiencies, which provide unpromising soil for cultural acquisitions—is what perpetuates so-called "racial inferiorities."

There is no such thing as racial or ethnic inferiority. A child, born among "savages," or "savage" parents, and transferred at a sufficiently tender age into a society which provides adequate training, may perfectly well become a scholar or a scientist.

Racial and ethnic superiority are as unreal as social superiority. The child of intellectuals, transferred at birth into a society of primitives, will exhibit the same general behavior as his adoptive parents.

We must get this quite clear. *Statistically*, the same capacity for intellectual coordination is common to every human being who is free from congenital deficiencies and is in normal health, and who has not suffered from dietetic deficiencies in early life; and this is true of every race and every society. But, of course, there are differences as between *individuals*. This individual differentiation occurs in animals too, and it was by taking his stand on physiological data that Pavlov was able to demonstrate the fact.

TYPOLOGY

The idea of individual differentiation goes back to Hippocrates (about 460-375 B.C.), who postulated the existence of *four* different basic *temperaments* in man: the sanguine, the choleric, the phlegmatic and the melancholic. It was indeed in honor of his illustrious predecessor that Pavlov, who also perceived *four* basic *types*, adopted the Hippocratic terms for his own purposes, but it must be admitted that the choice of words was somewhat unfortunate. Pavlov was as well aware of this as anybody else. He often spoke of an "almost insuperable difficulty in typological differentiation." Not only must we avoid using the terms "sanguine" or "phlegmatic," for example, in their everyday senses; we must also avoid any belief that there are rigid barriers between the various types, which are in any case still far from having been exhaustively defined. Here as elsewhere, there are borderline cases.

Pavlov, starting out from fortuitous observations, and proceeding beyond these to a large number of planned experiments, showed that there were various characteristic ways in which the nervous systems of different dogs might work. There were *weak* (or cowardly) dogs, and *strong* (or courageous) dogs. And the latter were divided into "non-equilibrated" and "equilibrated"; and these latter again (the equilibrated) were subdivided into the "mobile" and the "inert."

"This roughly corresponds," he explained, "to the classical system of temperaments. There are strong but unequilibrated animals, in which the processes of excitation and inhibition are both powerful, but in which excitation dominates inhibition; these are the *choleric* type of Hippocrates, the excitable, impulsive type. Then there are strong animals which are well equilibrated but have slow reactions: the *phlegmatic* type, calm and inert. Next there are other strong animals, deft and well equilibrated, the *sanguine* type, lively and mobile. Last come the weak animals in which inhibition dominates; they correspond to the *melancholic* type."

Where man was concerned he applied the following simplified outline: "The melancholic possesses an inhibited type of nervous system. Every phenomenon of existence acts on him as a restraining influence. He believes in nothing, hopes for nothing, sees and expects nothing but misfortune and danger. The choleric is manifestly the bellicose, impetuous type, easily and quickly roused. The phlegmatic is a worker, calm, steady, obstinate, persevering. The sanguine person is ardent, very productive, but only when there is plenty to be done and the work interests him; when this is not so he is inclined to boredom and laziness."

Typology offers no support whatever to any theory of aristocracy or race. It is strictly concerned with individuals, not societies and other human collectivities. It looks very much as if differentiation into types was the result of subtle differences in the arrangement of the neurons, and it does not appear to be—or at least, not in every case—hereditary.

In the U.S.S.R., Professor Anokhin and his collaborators have studied a two-headed human creature—hardly to be described as "Siamese twins"—which is eight years old, is not weak or sickly, and is of normal intellectual development. This freak of nature, which undoubtedly began life as a single fertilized ovum, consists of two little girls who are separate individuals as far as the diaphragm; from there downward they are one, with a single vascular system, a single genital system, and only two legs. They have two hearts, enclosed in a single pericardium; four lungs, four arms, two heads, and two entirely distinct nervous systems.

Contrary to all expectation, these two individuals, so closely joined, are of rather different nervous types. One—as we must say, since after all they are definitely two little girls—is calm and serious; the other is gay and excitable. They live under medical supervision with trained psychologists in attendance, and are being brought up in a thoroughly satisfactory environment. Both show normal intelligence.

However, one of them responds readily to the experiments in conditioning to which they are subjected; the other by no means so readily, *because she is against them.*

It seems that an initial conclusion should be drawn: individuals are born with different potentialities of character development even when they are of genetically identical origin. This precludes any mechanistic idea of social classes having a genetic foundation.

But even if basic types do sometimes show a hereditary basis, they can be much modified by environment. Two of Pavlov's assistants, Doctors Vyrzhikovsky and Mayorov, had the idea of separating a litter of puppies into two groups; those in the first group were kept in a cage from birth, the others were allowed to run free. On reaching maturity the first were timid, whereas the behavior of the others was normal.

It is clear that typology, the study of which is still in its infancy, ought to be used as a guide by psychologists, teachers and others interested in creating a genuinely human society; not a society of human robots, but one in which every individual has *equality of opportunity* and works according to his innate *means* so that everyone can live according to his *needs*. For no mere chance superiority, no inherited ability in coordination and creativeness, can ever justify preferential treatment for the individual concerned.

The physically or intellectually strong individual has no more rights than the weak; all he has is more duties, and his only reward should be satisfaction at being able to work more effectively (because more easily) for the good of the community. "All of us are harnessed to a common cause and each pulls his weight," said Pavlov. He was referring to the teamwork of his collaborators and himself, but he added: "My dream is that our joint work in the laboratory shall leave its mark in the attainment of human happiness."

4

Human Conditioning and Development

I HAVE tried to present Pavlov's achievement in as sober a light as possible; no paean of praise would have added to his glory. The importance of his work is recognized throughout the present-day world, even by people who pursue the study of reflexes and conveniently "forget" to mention his name. Certainly Pavlov did not say the last word on his subject, nor did he ever claim to have done so. Some of his conclusions are valid only as a first approximation—just as Newton's laws on gravitation are a first approximation. An example of such a conclusion is Pavlov's picture of the conditional connection.

At first, Pavlov thought this connection was built up between the cortical center responding to the new (conditional) stimulus, and, in the case of alimentary conditioned reflexes, centers in the hindbrain. Subsequently, on the basis of new data, he leaned toward the idea that the conditional connection was made exclusively in the hemispheres—more exactly, in the cerebral cortex—between the center reacting to the conditional stimulus and the cortical zone responsible for the regulation of the digestive center. (We are still referring to alimentary reflexes, but the principle is the same for all conditioning; different centers are concerned with different absolute stimuli, but that is all.)

"The formation of a new nervous pathway," he said at

this stage, "the process of connection, is effected entirely in the great hemispheres; that is to say, it is not only there that the points of response to innumerable indifferent stimuli are to be found, but also the command points representing the unconditioned reflexes, between which the connection is established. . . . The basic condition for the formation of a conditioned reflex is the association, the coincidence in time, of an excitation reaching a definite point in the *cortex* of the hemispheres, with a more intense excitation at another point, probably *also located in the cortex*; after a certain amount of time has elapsed an easier pathway is created between these two points."

However, in 1932 he said: "It can be affirmed that the subcortical structures are the source of energy for all higher nervous activity, and that the cortex plays the part of a regulator for this blind force, guiding and delicately controlling it."

But at that time it was still impossible to obtain experimental proof of this proposition, and the classical Pavlovian picture of conditional connection remains the one given above. Nevertheless, modern techniques of investigation and especially the use of microelectrodes, which allow us to explore at the level of the neuron itself (and even of its nucleus), seem likely to upset this conception. According to Professor Alfred Fessard, of the Collège de France, "We have collected much evidence to show that several subcortical structures also play a part in building new connections; indeed, it is ultimately more accurate to regard the construction of connections as calling into play nearly the whole of the brain, because of the close interdependence linking all the functional zones of which that organ is composed."

Pavlov, who never failed to emphasize the part played by his collaborators in his researches, would have been delighted to see his work completed by other people, and it was in fact one of his pupils, Professor Sarkisov (the present director of the Institute of the Brain in Moscow), who advised me to get in touch with Professor Fessard in order to discover the most recent views on conditioned reflexes and their mechanisms.

At the International Congress on the Electroencephalography of the Higher Nervous System (Moscow, 1960), Professor Fessard gave the following résumé of the conclusions arising out of his latest research: "The cortical structures are indispensable to the formation of a classical conditioned reflex, with its properties of extinction and of fine differentiation. Nevertheless, we are convinced that the initial associative operation takes place in the non-specific structures of reticular type,* among systems which are not differentiated in advance and which are therefore capable of assuming the new dynamic aspect imposed by some new associative pattern † of excitations, whether exteroceptive or interoceptive. The specific analyzers in the cortex do not appear to be absolutely indispensable in this operation, but they contribute to giving the conditioned reflex its definitive character as a *higher nervous activity*."

Other researchers have made emendations of a psychological kind. M. Jean-François Le Ny, for example, writes that the doctrine of reflexes "sometimes gives a meager, oversimplified picture of psychological reality," but he hastens to add: "Could it have been otherwise at the period when Pavlov was reaching his conclusions?"

Pavlov's work can only be reinforced by the modifications contributed to it by the work of later scientists. It would be an insult to Pavlov to try and preserve it unchanged, within the framework of the limitations imposed on him simply by the inadequate methods of observation with which he had to content himself. He would never have allowed anyone to fossilize his work, as some of his later followers have tried to do. Let us quote verbatim the verdict of M. Jean-François Le Ny: "It would be ridiculous to claim that human action, conduct and thought are 'reflexly conditioned' in the same sense as the salivation of Pavlov's dogs, but it is undoubtedly true that they are in some sort determined both as to their occurrence and their content, that they depend on the con-

* As a result of comments made by several of his colleagues, notably Jaspers and Sarkisov, Professor Fessard has qualified his remarks thus: "The term 'reticular' is used here in a general sense, to denote a type of diffuse interneuronic connection, as against the laminated type found in the cortices and the nuclear type found in the gray subcortical structures. In using it we are therefore referring neither to what anatomists call the *formatio reticularis,* nor even to what is sometimes designated by the wider, more inclusive term, 'reticular system.' "

† This word is in English in the original. Grey Walter (*The Living Brain,* p. 40) has an interesting passage on the use of the word. (*Tr.*)

ditions, present and past, individual and social, in which men live and act; and this process of determination is not radically different from that which rules conditioning. Human nervous and psychical activity is a single entity; it comprises different levels of complexity, a hierarchy of functions, a *de facto* and *de jure* pre-eminence of higher activities over lower, but this is a very different thing from a division into two territories, one being that of the body, of physiology and conditioning, and the other that of spiritual essence, of thought beyond the reach of law, and of absolute freedom from cause and effect. Freedom for the individual does not lie in denying his own conditioning or in a vain hope of emancipating himself from it by refusing to conform to it; freedom lies, rather, in a rational, scientific awareness of the conditions determining that freedom, and of a planned effort to change them for the better."

The following remark of M. Victor Lafitte, a commentator on Pavlov's outlook, therefore remains completely valid: "Pavlov has contributed a new confirmation of the fundamental tenet of historical materialism, according to which there is no such thing as 'eternal human nature'; the reason being that man is susceptible of being transformed through the modification of the material conditions in which he lives. Thus socialist society, in conformity with its fundamental law—namely to ensure the maximum satisfaction of the continually growing needs, both material and cultural, of society as a whole—has set itself, here and now, the problem of prolonging life and suppressing a multitude of morbid processes. Pavlov has helped us to understand that, in Marx's words, 'if circumstances shape man, we must shape circumstances in a human way.' "

THE GOAL-SEEKING REFLEX

It was only toward the end of his life, after collecting an abundant harvest of observations on animals—first dogs, then monkeys—that Pavlov turned his attention to the human realm. Unfortunately, this endeavor to reach a synthesis was cut short by his death. Nevertheless, he had long noted, in men as in animals, the presence of two important general innate reflexes which were the point of departure for a host of activities and reactions which sometimes came under the governance work of other, more specific reflexes, and sometimes transcended them. In discussing them—the "goal-seeking reflex" and the "reflex of liberty"—we emphasize that Pavlov himself had not taken them beyond the stage of a first sketch.

Early in his work he saw in the goal-seeking reflex the origin of the strange urge which makes some animals hoard food, or amass objects which are of no use to them (as the magpie does); an urge which is also found in a magnified form in man, as "collector's mania," and which in the human context can even give rise to avarice—for the miser, according to Pavlov, is simply a "collector of money."

This is how he explained the origin of the goal-seeking reflex: "Every day, we are attracted by various substances that are necessary for the chemical equilibrium of our own bodies. We ingest these substances and are thereby satisfied for a while. Then, a few hours later, we are seized once more by desire for these alimentary substances. At the same time, every new stimulus reaching us provokes in us some action designed to tell us more about the nature of that stimulus. We gaze at some new sight, listen to some new sound, sniff strongly when we encounter a new smell, and if the object under consideration is within reach of our hands we try to take hold of it; in a word, we constantly endeavor to apprehend new phenomena by using the receptive surfaces with which we are endowed, our sense organs. . . . The constant daily application of these grasping reflexes, and many others of the same kind, has resulted in the formation, through heredity, of a general prehensile reflex aimed at any object which arrests our attention for the first time. There are several ways in which this generalization may have taken place; two mechanisms, in particular, are easy to imagine. In the first place, the irradiation of the excitation involved in these grasping reflexes, whenever the excitation reaches a high pitch, causes, for example, a child to put any object which attracts it into its mouth (a matter of common observation). There may also be, thanks to coincidence in time, an association between objects of every kind and various grasping reflexes. The kinship between the goal-seeking reflex and its typical form, hoarding, on the one hand, and the feeding reflex, the principal form of the grasping reflex, on the other, is clearly shown by the identity between the characteristic features of these two reflexes (the main feature of both of them consists of seizing the object; this is followed by satisfaction and then indifference)."

In this goal-seeking reflex we can also see the origin of stealing, which assumes the character commonly conferred on it only when the individual becomes aware that it is an antisocial act. Does a kitten or a puppy *steal,* in the sense of wrong-doing, when it slips into the larder to snatch some titbit or other which, through the mechanism of the conditioned reflex, has set its limbs moving? Of course not. The human young is a thief too (in an innocent sense); instinctively so. What prevents us from being thieves is upbringing, the conditioning which inhibits the reflex of grasping and appropriating. Many thieves are mentally retarded individuals whose cortical structures are incomplete and in whom it is impossible for the innate impulses to be efficiently controlled. According to the psychiatrist Lévy-Valensi, "Pathological stealing springs from a variety of causes. Among them are the exaggeration of normal needs (as in oligophrenia and dementia)—such is the case with ordinary delinquents; the exaggeration of abnormal needs (as in drug addicts and sexual perverts); exaggerated unconsciousness (retarded, confused and depressed people); the loss of the idea of property (as in dementia, debility, delirium, and manic states); and combinations of these causes."

In the *Manuel alphabétique de Psychiatrie,* from which the foregoing is quoted, we also read: "In dementia, acts of theft are unconscious or amnesic; they are performed without precautions and may be reiterated. They are absurd (useless objects are stolen), and the condition is sometimes complicated by collector's mania."

But are not property and ownership fundamentally connected with the reflex of appropriation? To raise the question of their deep-lying identity with theft, scientifically speaking, does not in the least imply a wish to whitewash or defend theft. In our view, both appropriation and stealing are antisocial gestures—and both could be combated by inhibitory conditioned reflexes!

In a wider context, the goal-seeking reflex (of which the grasping and appropriating reflexes, in the present writer's opinion, are merely derivatives) is indeed, as Pavlov said, an aid to man's development, both individual and communal. He wrote: "A beautiful, intense life is lived only by the man who, all his life long, pursues a goal which is attainable yet never attained, or the man who, with similar ardor, passes from one goal to another. All progress and culture are a function of this goal-seeking reflex. There are all sorts of ways of being a collector; one can collect trivial objects, or one can collect knowledge; one can even *collect* goals, as for example do the economists (the improvement of living conditions); and scientists (scientific discovery); and philanthropists (generous deeds); and so on.

"Life," he concluded, "loses its attraction when it no longer has any purpose. Suicides do away with themselves because they feel life has lost its meaning. Their tragedy consists in having been unable to surmount a temporary phase of inhibition of the goal-seeking reflex."

Man pursues innumerable goals; indeed, there is no limit to them. But, at the risk of repeating ourselves, it seems to us that the first, the most important goal is to destroy the proprietary, monopolistic aspect of the all-embracing goal-seeking reflex, by creating a society in which everyone shall "have according to his needs." And Pavlov, who in 1917 hailed "the disappearance of the deep gulf sundering the rich from the poor in Russia," would assuredly have been of the same opinion.

THE REFLEX OF LIBERTY

"The reflex of liberty," said Pavlov, "is a general reaction in animals. It is one of the most important innate reflexes. Without it, the smallest obstacle encountered by the animal would suffice to modify the course of its life completely."

The existence of this reflex of liberty had been made clear to him by the behavior of a dog which, as soon as it was placed under the conditions of restraint necessary for experimental work, salivated spontaneously and continuously and was thus useless for research purposes.

"As we knew already from previous observations," says Pavlov, "this salivation is the result of a general excitation and usually accompanies a reaction of breathlessness, somewhat similar to what is called being 'excited' or 'agitated.' Dogs are frequently subject to this condition in the early days of their experiences in the laboratory, especially dogs that are not very tame. This one, on the contrary, which was very gentle and had quickly made friends with us, ought normally to have been exempt from it. Yet the excitation went on for a whole month, even on the experimental stand. We then decided to study this peculiarity more closely. For two weeks, the dog was tethered on a work table in an isolated room. The condition persisted. The conditioned reflex which we were creating in the dog was slow to form, remained weak, and was subject to fluctuations. The spontaneous salivation continued and even seemed to increase in the course of the experimental session. At the same time the dog was restless, struggling with its harness, biting and scratching the stand, and so on, and its breathing became correspondingly faster as the session proceeded. At the beginning of each session the dog would immediately take the food that was offered to it in order to form the conditioned reflex, but would subsequently accept it only after a longer and longer lapse of time, and would sometimes refuse to eat at all unless the food was actually forced into its mouth."

Pavlov, and his assistant, Dr. Goubergritz, who had been the first to notice this very unusual behavior, set themselves first of all to discover the origin of the continuous secretory reaction, and of the defensive motor reactions which were so completely at variance with the animal's friendly nature at other times; in short, they wanted to know what, in the given conditions, caused the excitation.

It was true that some dogs had already shown that they were upset by being placed on a raised stand. As soon as they were put back on the ground they quieted down. Others could not stand being alone and had to have the experimenter beside them to keep them company. But this particular dog responded to none of these alleviations. The researchers thought its harness might be too tight and might be hurting or even injuring it, but nothing happened when the straps were loosened, and the obvious conclusion had to be accepted: *the dog was intolerant of all restraint;* it remained quiet and stopped salivating only when completely free; and in that state it could even be effectively conditioned.

In order to prove beyond question the innate character of what he called, from now on, the "reflex of liberty," Pavlov arranged for the dog to fast completely for twenty-four hours. This inhibited the reaction not at all: the alimentary reflex proved to be weaker than the reflex of liberty—and yet, as we have seen, the alimentary reflex is so strong that it can inhibit the reflex of pain.

"There is an essential difference between these two experiments," writes Pavlov. "In the conditioned reflex produced by a painful stimulus the alimentary and destructive reflexes coincide almost perfectly (brief alimentary stimulation, equally brief painful stimulation). In the other case the alimentary stimulation is also brief, but the reflex of liberty persists throughout the experiment and becomes more intense the longer the animal remains on the stand."

It was then decided that this excessively freedom-loving animal should not be fed except on the experimental stand. "For ten days," Pavlov records, "it ate sparingly and steadily lost weight; then it gradually began to eat more until it consumed the whole of its daily ration; but three months of experimenting went by before the reflex of liberty was extinguished. The elements of which this reflex is composed disappear only gradually."

But the conditioned reflexes set up in this dog never reached a high degree of intensity, and were subject to partial inhibition. When the practice of feeding the dog exclusively on the stand had been discontinued, the reflex of liberty returned and soon regained all its old force.

"The return of this reflex," comments Pavlov, "shows how strong it is, and demonstrates its innate character. It also eliminates any other interpretation of the reaction in question."

Though the experimental technique perhaps left a little to be desired, it is hardly possible to deny the existence of a reflex of liberty in all animals generally, since it is well known how hard it is to accustom some species (the wild cat, for example) to accept confinement in zoological gardens and to breed in those conditions. But as a counterpart of the reflex of liberty is there also an innate "reflex of servility"?

Pavlov's answer was in the affirmative. He postulated that this reflex protected the weak against the strong: a gesture of submission had the effect of arresting a gesture of aggression (he cited the example of a little dog lying on its back at the approach of a big dog).* It was his opinion that this reflex could also be found in man, and he attempted a description of it in a paper, using the term "reflex of serfdom."

Curiously, this paper was submitted to the Petrograd Biological Society in May, 1917, only a few months before the Revolution. Pavlov deplored that the "reflex of serfdom" was so often to be found in Russia "in the most varied forms."

* Konrad Lorenz, in his book, *King Solomon's Ring,* gives a lively and amusing discussion of this. (*Tr.*)

He asked that people become aware of it the better to struggle for its extirpation, as the reflex of serfdom led to inhibition of the goal-seeking reflex: "Serfdom has turned the serf into a passive individual, without desires, his most legitimate aspirations having been stifled by the will and the whims of his rulers."

THE PROBLEM OF SLEEP

One of the problems which most interested Pavlov was that of sleep. It is a matter of empirical observation that sleep is a "reparative" process, but of what does it consist and what is its mechanism?

As we ascend the evolutionary scale we find that the higher the animal, the stronger the need for sleep. Even invertebrates need sleep; ants do, for example. Among vertebrates, it has been found that some kinds of fish sleep. Sleep also occurs in batrachians, and still more in reptiles. It is yet more clearly marked in birds, and, as everyone can observe, all mammals sleep.

Grave disturbance, not only psychical but also physiological, can result from lack of sleep. At the beginning of the present century Professor Henri Piéron carried out an experiment with dogs which was conclusive in this respect. By having them led about without any chance of respite, he subjected several subjects to long periods of wakefulness; death supervened after a period which varied from ten to seventeen days in different dogs. When he took spinal fluid from a sleepless dog and injected it into one which had been allowed to sleep as much as it wanted to, the second dog immediately displayed an uncontrollable urge to sleep. Professor Piéron inferred that lack of sleep caused a kind of cellular intoxication attended by the production of a substance which he tried to isolate, and to which he gave the name *hypnotoxin.* He postulated that hypnotoxin had the property of gravely damaging neuronic structures. And autopsy of animals that had died of experimental insomnia did in fact reveal various lesions of the nervous centers.

But we must not jump to the conclusion that sleep is caused by a process of cellular intoxication. "We sleep," said Piéron, "not because we are intoxicated, but in order not to become so." He regarded sleep as being ultimately caused by an innate reflex. He even added: "If for convenience of expression we may talk of hypnotoxin, it is understood that we must not let the word deceive us into creating a new entity. I would say that the substance's properties are connected with the disintegration of the cerebral albuminoids found in the cerebrospinal fluid."

The hypothesis of Brown-Séquard (1817-94) was that "sleep involves cortical inhibition through the generalization of one of the processes which form part of the normal functioning of the brain." This was the line explored by Pavlov. He had noticed that as soon as a dog was alone in an isolated room, and in position for experimental work, it became drowsy. Gradually this drowsiness shaded off into deep sleep. Sleep also developed under the influence of active stimuli "which had been used in the formation of powerful conditional stimuli." Some dogs were particularly prone to react in this way.

The occurrence of sleep, or at least drowsiness, in circumstances of monotony is a matter of ordinary observation. People feel drowsy in waiting rooms, for example, even though they may be conversing at the time, if the conversation is a very dull one. Sometimes a lecture makes one drowsy; the present writer will even admit to having dozed off while *giving* a lecture!—so glaring was his audience's lack of interest in the scientific question presented, with which he himself was thoroughly familiar through having lectured on it a number of times before, but which was clearly above the head of the average listener. Again, some people fall asleep at the theater or the cinema, or while performing work of some monotonous, hackneyed kind.

But Pavlov was not content with superficial conclusions. He decided to analyze the sleep process with all possible rigor. He noticed that as long as the animal's attention was aroused (first by the arranging of various kinds of apparatus to prepare it for the experiment, and then by direct stimulation, whether absolute or conditional), no drowsiness appeared. But, he says, "it is enough that there should be the gap of a minute between the end of the preparations and the beginning of the experimental work, for the initial phase of sleep to supervene. Ten minutes later, if work has still not begun, a second phase appears."

So far, this presents nothing which is not a matter of ordinary observation, except for the exact noting of the lapse of time. We might simply content ourselves with concluding that the dog was "bored," like a human being; but this would not advance us an inch in the study of the *physiological causes* of sleep. Pavlov, who had already demonstrated the irradiation of both excitations and inhibitions in the cortex, and, like Brown-Séquard before him, had felt intuitively that an inhibitory mechanism was concerned, continued his researches with the help of the secretory reflex, which had already served him so well.

"During the experiment in which there was no drowsiness," he said, "we were confronted by two reactions on the animal's part: on the one hand a secretory action—saliva was flowing; on the other hand, a motor reaction—the animal took the food offered to it. In other words, there were two reflexes, one secretory, the other motor.

"Now, under the influence of the hypnogenic environment (the animal is alone, fitted up with measuring equipment), the processes develop as follows: two minutes after the preparations have been completed, during which lapse of time the animal had been inactive, we put the conditional stimulus into action; the first phase of sleep is then observed, and it is manifested by the *disappearance of the secretory reflex*. The conditional stimulus has ceased to take effect, yet if we offer food the animal seizes it, which proves that the motor reflex is still present.

"If the dog is kept waiting for ten minutes before the experiment begins, the drowsiness is deeper, but the reaction observed is quite different: strange to say, *salivation takes place but the animal does not seize the food*. It not only does not take it, but visibly turns away from it. The second phase of sleep therefore involves inhibition of the motor reaction, whereas the secretory reaction is no longer inhibited.

"Finally, if the dog is left in its soporific surroundings for a period lasting from half an hour to one hour before the beginning of the experiment, a *complete deep sleep* sets in, and both reflexes vanish."

If the animal is to be used for experimental work, it must, naturally, be woken first. This can be done abruptly or in stages. For abrupt waking Pavlov used a very loud rattle; this at once roused the animal to the fully waking state, with secretory and motor reactions ready to function normally. As for waking by stages, "One of the customary methods of gradually dispelling sleep is to feed the dog at definite intervals; feeding may even be begun with the forcible introduction of food into the mouth. Then you can observe the phases described above but in reverse order. After the deep sleep the secretory reflex is present but the dog does not take the food. Later on, the secretory reflex fails to appear; however, the dog eats. And finally, after frequent repetitions of the feeding, both reflexes reappear."

Pavlov and his fellow workers varied these experiments, carefully measuring secretions and reaction times. Apart from various subsidiary conclusions which can be omitted here, the inference is that sleep depends on the appearance of what Dr. Chauchard calls "waves of internal inhibition destroying the delicate mosaic of excitation and inhibition which is normally present in the waking state."

Whence comes this wave of inhibition? Today we are in a position to say that it starts from a veritable "sleep center," though Pavlov would not concede this at the time of his experiments; proof was afforded only with the help of EEG. And as a result of von Economo's research we know that the center is situated in the hypothalamus.

Primarily, sleep is innate; a baby sleeps by instinct, not by a conditioned reflex. In the same way both adults and animals, with differences as between individuals and as between species, sleep for a certain portion of the twenty-four hours. But sleep can also result from a conditioned reflex, and the credit for demonstrating the fact undoubtedly belongs to Pavlov. The physical and chemical changes causing the inhibition of the centers in sleep have been studied by Sherrington, Bremer, Lapicque, A. and B. Chauchard, Drabovitch and others; the last three named, following up the work of Lapicque, have studied the chronaxie of the neurons in the progressive disconnection of the various nervous circuits.

For sleep, as we said above, sets up a state of "super-repose" in the cortical neurons following a kind of "uncoupling" between the sense organs and the coordinating centers. These centers nevertheless continue to function, since by means of EEG we can record their activity in the shape of wave forms which represent changes in electric potential (and we would remind the reader that any cell ceasing to effect metabolic changes, which produce energy and therefore electricity, would die).

If it must be granted that the mesencephalon possesses a sleep-producing zone, it should also be borne in mind that the mechanism of sleep is not for that reason a simple one. The hypothalamus and the formatio reticularis play the leading roles, but the sleep centers are no doubt themselves governed by metabolic factors. Dr. Laborit has recently shown that a metabolic cycle in the cell, with a twenty-four-hour rhythm (not twenty-four hours as such, but night and day), involves the formation of a substance related to gamma aminobutyric acid: sodium 4-hydroxyburate, which acts more or less directly to inhibit the centers and induce the physiological state we call sleep.

This in no way invalidates the conception of a hypothalamic "sleep center"; it simply points to the mechanism by which this center brings about the disconnection of the synapses and, consequently, isolates the sense receptors from the centers. Nor does Dr. Laborit's thesis seem to conflict with the observations of Piéron, whose hypothetical hypnotoxin does not cause sleep but arises from the lack of it, which would lead logically to a disturbance of the metabolic cycle.

All this is at once a question of innate reflexes and of biochemistry. At the time of writing, Laborit is studying the possibility of inducing sleep by a chemical agent consisting essentially of sodium 4-hydroxyburate. Other chemical agents, by intensifying the metabolic reactions of the cells, notably oxidation, would suspend the manufacture of the sleep producing substance.

But is that not exactly what we do ourselves, whenever we feel drowsy and go out for "a breath of fresh air" to wake ourselves up—thereby making our nerve endings respond to new stimuli, which in turn cause the centers to be coupled up again? And, on the other hand, surely any monotonous condition which induces drowsiness causes us to take in less oxygen and consequently slows down our cellular metabolism, which then starts manufacturing the sleep-producing substance. And whenever we stay awake by an act of will, what are we doing if not quickening our metabolism and fighting against waves of inhibition? Pavlov's theories would seem not to contradict contemporary research, but to be enriched by it.

FROM SLEEP TO HYPNOSIS

No doubt I shall shock at once the admirers of Pavlov and those of Freud, if I maintain that at some future time a constructive synthesis will have to be made between psychoanalysis and the study of reflexes. But in fact the two men expressed parallel views on one subject, namely hypnosis: "One of the peculiar features of the hypnotic state," said Freud, "is a sort of paralysis of the will and the power of movement; a paralysis produced by the influence of an omnipotent person on a defenseless, impotent subject. This feature is reminiscent of the hypnosis produced in animals by fear." Pavlov thought that animal hypnosis was a reflex of self-preservation: if the animal could not seek safety in flight or fight, it immobilized itself, and it seemed as if this immobility had the power of halting the enemy's attack.

This is not just an ingenious idea. The phenomenon, while it cannot be promoted to the rank of a general law applying to all species, has often been observed. Many a rash or unwary hunter has been saved by shamming dead. A bull does not attack a matador who stands motionless in the arena. On the other hand, a cat will run after anything that moves—not only a mouse, but a leaf, or a cork on a string. And in the farmyard, if the cat runs away the cock chases it.

If we suddenly turn a dog over onto its back, so that it is too surprised to fight against assuming this unnatural attitude, and if we hold it in that position for a while (a short time is usually enough) and then take our hands away, the dog will remain lying on its back for many minutes or even hours. Why so? Pavlov's explanation is that "the phenomenon represents a self-protecting reflex of an inhibitory character. Faced with an overwhelming power, from which there is no escape in struggle or in flight, the animal's only chance of salvation is to remain immobile in order not to be noticed, since moving objects attract particular attention, or not to provoke by fussy, restless movements an aggressive reaction on the part of this overwhelming force."

This is not tactical calculation, but pure reflex action, beyond voluntary control (on the other hand, it is will power which enables the subject to resist hypnosis or ward off sleep). "Immobility," Pavlov goes on, "is brought about in the following manner: Extraordinary external stimuli, highly intense or very unusual in form, first of all cause a rapid reflex inhibition of the motor region of the cerebral cortex which controls the so-called voluntary movements. Depending on the intensity and duration of the stimulus, this inhibition is either confined to the motor region and does not pass to other regions of the cerebral hemispheres and to the midbrain, or it irradiates over all these parts. In the first case there are present reflexes of the eye muscles (the animal follows the experimenter with its eyes), of the glands (when food is offered, there begins a secretion of saliva, although no skeletal movements in the direction of food are observed), and, finally, tonic reflexes from the midbrain to the skeletal muscles in order to retain the position into which the animal has been brought (catalepsy). In the second case all the above-mentioned reflexes gradually disappear, and the animal passes into an absolutely passive, sleeping state accompanied by a general relaxation of the musculature. This course of the phenomena is further confirmation of the conclusion . . . that the so-called inhibition is nothing more than sleep, but partial and localized. It is clear that the rigidity and stupor which seize us in cases of great fear is nothing else but the above-described reflex."

Pavlov did not use only the method of laying the animal on its back; he also succeeded in showing that hypnosis, like sleep, could be brought about by the prolonged action of monotonous stimuli which finally brought the corresponding cortical cells to a state of inhibition. "This inhibition, on the one hand, is of different degrees of intensity, and, on the other hand, spreads to a greater or lesser extent over the cerebral cortex and further down the brain. . . . [Continued observation] revealed a greater variety of symptoms of the hypnotic state, its more and more delicate gradations, which hardly differ from the wakeful state, and its ever-increasing mobility depending on the slightest changes in the surroundings, on insignificant modifications in the external stimuli acting upon the animal."

He and his partner in these experiments, Dr. Petrova, noticed that two of the dogs they habitually used invariably fell into a hypnotic state the moment they were placed in the usual experimental conditions and respectively equipped. "One of the dogs, which was usually in a less profound hypnotic state, distinctly exhibited what in mental diseases is called negativism.* After a conditioned stimulation applied during a certain period of time, we put food before the dog; the latter turns away from the food receptacle. But when we begin to move the receptacle away, the dog makes a movement in

* "Negativism or contralism—a negative attitude toward the influences of the surrounding world; one of the fundamental symptoms of catatonia and of other schizophrenic forms; it is also met with in other mental disorders" (editor's note in I. P. Pavlov, *Selected Works,* Moscow: Foreign Languages Publishing House, 1955). (*Tr.*)

its direction. We present the receptacle anew; the dog turns toward it once more. We have termed the reaction of turning away from the food receptacle negative, or the first phase of negativism, and the movement toward the food receptacle—positive, or the second phase. This negativism may recur many times until the animal at last partakes of the food, which happens in most cases. The degree of hypnosis is expressed precisely by the number of repetitions of this procedure."

We have described here only one of the problems of hypnosis studied by Pavlov. Not all of the many notes he published on the subject, and on the pathology of the nervous system in general, established anything very definite in the way of conclusions, and while they are of considerable interest to specialists, their highly technical nature is beyond the scope of this book.*

Let us now take an equally brief glance at some aspects of his work on mental illnesses.

EXPERIMENTAL NEUROSES

All writers on the subject agree that neuroses in man are caused by "conflicts." In the eyes of psychoanalysts these conflicts are sexual, and consist, broadly speaking, of a struggle between instinct and upbringing. Psychosomatic medicine shows that neurotic symptoms proceed from functional nervous disequilibrium. Unlike the psychoses, or at least those psychoses whose origins are known, the neuroses have no organic basis. Neurosis also differs from most cases of psychosis in that, while it affects the patient's psychical life and leads him into unusual behavior, it does not submerge his personality. Consequently, neurotic subjects evince a painful and often excessive awareness of their morbid state.

It must undoubtedly be admitted that because of the conditions of modern life, with its perpetual conflict between what we do and what we would like to do, very few of us are entirely free from neurosis; and the more intellectually active the individual the truer does this become, since an intelligent, educated man inevitably confronts himself with more prob-

* Hypnosis comprises three phases: (*a*) the *equalization* state, in which all stimuli, whatever their strength, act with equal force; (*b*) the *paradoxical,* in which weaker stimuli are more effective than stronger ones; (*c*) the *ultraparadoxical,* in which inhibitory stimuli cause a positive effect, and positive stimuli an inhibitory effect.

lems to solve than an uneducated one. Neurosis is almost unknown among primitives, and animals are rarely neurotic. Nevertheless, Pavlov succeeded in producing experimental neuroses in dogs, and his work has thrown a revealing light on the physiological mechanism of neurosis, which develops all the more clearly in proportion as the subject approximates to the congenitally "excitable" type (membership of this type confers a physiological and psychological predisposition to neurosis, just as intellectuality does in the case of man). The more equilibrated the individual, in the typological sense, the harder is it for neurosis to arise; this holds good for dogs as well as humans.

It will be recalled that a conditioned reflex can be set up by means of a painful stimulus. (Pain is something like a sixth sense: it is transmitted to the hemispheres not by the tactile papillae but by special receptors.) If we conduct a powerful electric current to some part of a dog's skin, the dog will react according to its "character," either by flight or ferocity; but if we simultaneously offer food to it, in accordance with the classical procedure of experiments in conditioning, we shall find it quite easy to build up a conditioned reflex, especially if the dog is hungry. Soon, as we noted in an earlier chapter, it will salivate eagerly at the application of the conditional stimulus alone (provided, of course, that this stimulus has been reinforced from time to time by the absolute stimulus); it will salivate, in other words, when we are "hurting" it.

Having firmly established such a reflex, Pavlov began changing the spot at which the current was applied, gradually moving the electrodes further and further from the original place of application. The conditional stimulus was used by itself in this way, and the reflex continued to act until a certain distance had been covered; then, suddenly, the distance from the original place having been once more increased, a radical change took place: the dog produced a very strong defensive reaction and the conditioned reflex vanished without trace. What was more, from this time onward even the application of the weakest current to the original spot did not produce salivation, but did produce a powerful reaction of self-defense.

In another dog treated in exactly the same way, the disappearance of the conditioned reflex and its replacement by movements of attack came about much sooner. To sum up the rest of the matter briefly, both animals got into such an excited state that they had to be rested for three months, "and even after this interim we succeeded in establishing the reflex, very slowly and with a very weak current, only in one of the two; the other was stubbornly resistant."

Here is something subtler still: "A conditioned alimentary reflex was brought about in a dog by a circle of light projected onto a screen placed in front of the animal. We then began to elaborate a differentiation of the circle from an ellipse of the same size and intensity of light, i.e. the appearance of the circle was accompanied each time by feeding, whereas that of the ellipse was not. In this way the differentiation was obtained. The circle evoked an alimentary reaction, but the ellipse remained ineffective, which, as we know, is a result of development of inhibition. The ellipse which was applied first greatly differed in form from the circle (the proportion of its axes was 2 : 1). Then the form of the ellipse was brought closer and closer to that of the circle, i.e. the axes of the ellipse were gradually equalized, and thus sooner or later we were able to obtain an increasingly delicate differentiation. But when we applied an ellipse whose axes were as 9 : 8, the picture abruptly changed. The new delicate differentiation, which always remained incomplete, persisted for two or three weeks, after which it not only disappeared itself, but caused the loss of all earlier, even the least delicate, differentiations. . . . All differentiations had to be elaborated anew. . . . When the final differentiation was reached, the same story was repeated —all the differentiations vanished, and the dog again became excited."

In both cases (that of the alimentary secretion in response to a painful electric current, and that of the differentiation of the ellipses from the circle), the inhibitory process was deranged with lasting results. "For," says Pavlov, "in the first case, the defense reaction is what ought to have been inhibited. In the second case, the differentiation is based on inhibition; its disappearance therefore denotes a disturbance of inhibition. . . . We feel justified in *affirming* that *the collision between two contrary processes, one of excitation and the other of inhibition, which were difficult to accommodate simultaneously or too unusual in duration or intensity, or both, causes a breakdown of equilibrium.*"

It may be noted that some dogs put up with these disequilibrating situations quite easily, or at least put up with them to some extent. This chiefly applies to dogs of the "strong equilibrated" type in the Pavlovian typology.

TYPOLOGY AND MENTAL ILLNESS

It is not our concern to put up a case for the superiority of the therapeutic methods adopted in Soviet psychiatry as a result of Pavlov's influence, though there is no doubt that Soviet specialists have been obtaining brilliant results for many years merely by means of *natural sleep* or the simple remedy of bromide, while the use of drastic measures, such as lobotomy, is absolutely forbidden in the U.S.S.R.

"The normal state of higher nervous functioning," says Pavlov, "is equilibrium between the processes constituting that activity. The disturbance of this equilibrium is illness. But even a relatively normal state often hides some degree of disequilibrium. Nervous pathology is related to the type of higher nervous activity; thus, under very taxing experimental conditions, the dogs which soonest and most readily showed signs of nervous disturbance belonged to the extreme types, the excitable and the weak, although by using powerful means it is also possible to shatter the equilibrium of the best equilibrated strong types."

Nervous disequilibrium is caused, essentially, by overstrain—either of the processes of excitation or those of inhibition, or by the collision of the two processes (see the example in the previous section, of the creation of a positive conditioned reflex to a circle and an inhibitory reflex to an ellipse).

"In the excitable type," says Pavlov, "neurosis appears in the following way: the inhibitory process, which is normally very weak in comparison with the process of excitation, becomes still weaker and almost disappears; the extinction of the processes of excitation is much slowed down, etc. The animals become greatly agitated and can no longer be controlled; they do their utmost to escape from their harness or else, on the contrary, fall into an inert, sleepy state never previously observed in them.

"Neurosis in the weak type has an almost exclusively depressive character. The conditioned reflexes are obtained in any order, and, more frequently still, disappear completely. In the experimental situation the animal is almost always in a hypnotic state, and exhibits the different phases of hypnosis (there is no conditioned reflex and the animal does not even take the food offered to it)."

Such neuroses in dogs are astonishingly like neurasthenia in human beings, whether in the manic or the depressive form. They also show resemblances to traumatic neuroses and some other psychopathological phenomena.

Toward the close of his career, Pavlov sometimes divided human beings into three types: the intellectual, the artist and the intermediate type, according to the use made of the signal systems: the *artist* using mainly the first signal system (direct stimuli), the *intellectual* using mainly the second signal system (conceptual language and its corollary, writing). He believed that in pathological cases of disequilibrium between the two systems the intellectual tended toward psychasthenia (which Janet had interpreted as being caused by a more or less congenital weakness of psychical activity, aggravated by fatigue or emotional strain), whereas the artist tended toward hysteria (which Hesnard * called "the neurosis of expression," since he regarded the hysterical subject as someone simulating, but in good faith).

"In hysterical persons," Pavlov observes, "general weakness, naturally, has a special effect on the second signaling system, which in the artistic type in any case yields pride of place to the first system, while in normally developed persons the second signaling system is the highest regulator of human behavior. Hence the chaotic character of the activity of the first signaling system and of the emotional fund in the form of pathological fantasies and unrestrained emotivity with profound destruction of the general nervous equilibrium (sometimes paralyses, at others contractures,† or convulsive fits or lethargy) and in particular, synthesis of personality.

"In psychasthenics the general weakness, naturally, again affects the basic foundation of the correlations between the organism and environment—namely, the first signaling system and the emotional fund. Hence the absence of a sense of reality, continual feeling of inferiority of life, complete

* Eminent French psychoanalyst; see Chapter V of *Sigmund Freud and Psychoanalysis*, by Gérard Lauzun (in this series). (*Tr.*)

† "Convulsive contraction of certain groupings of muscles which in hysterical persons sometimes lasts for months, and years" (editor's note in I. P. Pavlov, *Selected Works*, Moscow, 1955).

inadequacy in life together with constant fruitless and perverted cogitation in the form of obsessions and phobias."

It may be added that, starting from the study of these same general types or rather the two extreme types, the strong disequilibrated and the weak disequilibrated, the great psychiatrist Kretschmer, Pavlov's contemporary, connected manic-depressive psychosis with the former, and schizophrenia with the latter.

"PAINLESS CHILDBIRTH"

At a clinic in Sofia, Bulgaria, I once watched the birth of a child whose mother had been conditioned by the psychoprophylactic method created after Pavlov's death, but deriving directly from his research and teaching. Obviously, such an event as childbirth does not take place to order; it was just my good luck to be there at the time. I marveled at the results obtained: though one cannot say pain had been totally eliminated, my impression was, nevertheless, that I was watching a process which had reached a maximum of normality and which was not traumatic.*

The idea of applying conditioning to the elimination of pain in childbirth goes back to 1912. It started from a brilliant thesis by Dr. N. Erofeeva, a disciple of Pavlov, who argued that since pain was irradiated in the cortex through the stimulation of specific centers, and that since it was possible to set up a conditioned reflex which inhibited another reflex (innate or acquired), pain in childbirth could be abolished by means of conditioned reflexes.

The two names principally associated with the development of the modern method of psychoprophylaxis are those of Doctors Velvovsky † and Platonov. In 1920, Velvovsky

* I have written "painless childbirth" both because it is the literal translation of *l'accouchement sans douleur* and because it is the accepted technical expression in English. However, I have heard of a teacher of the technique who strongly prefers the expression "childbirth without distress": pain, she says, is not necessarily abolished altogether by psychoprophylaxis, though it can be reduced to insignificance. What is eliminated is fear and distress, and their power to magnify pain and its effects (*Tr.*)

† See the Bibliography. It should perhaps be mentioned that the volume in question is a scientific treatise of a highly technical nature; it is not, and was not intended to be by its authors, a manual for expectant mothers. (*Tr.*)

wrote: "Pavlov's teaching has reinforced our conviction that childbirth, as a natural action, is not of necessity accompanied by pain. Pain in childbirth is not an inborn phenomenon, that is to say we are not dealing with something immutable and hereditary. Our objective is therefore not to seek ways of 'curing' or attentuating the pains of parturition, but rather to explain their origin. Our view is that parturition, as an essentially natural phenomenon, cannot be classed as a traumatic event and consequently should not be made the object of a therapy."

Thus a philosophical point of view is what underlies the creation of a "psychoprophylactic method" for ensuring "painless childbirth": the aim is to inhibit, by means of a new conditioning, the widely diffused biblical text according to which the Almighty laid upon woman the famous curse that "in sorrow shalt thou bring forth children."

Obviously the subject admits of endless argument. In some circumstances, notably if the fetus is presented in a difficult position or the mother's pelvis is abnormally narrow, pain from purely mechanical causes is unavoidable. In this matter, as in others, one cannot afford to dogmatize. Women have undergone real suffering in childbirth, and still do, without ever having heard of the "sin of Eve" and the divine wrath which it is supposed to have called down. It has, nonetheless, been established that among primitives, childbirth usually takes place without any traumatic effects; it even seems to be an insignificant event which fits in with the round of domestic activities and does not interrupt them. Indeed, it is a known fact that in some tribes it is the father who suffers!—or rather who, during his wife's labor, shows symptoms of pain which doubtless are not entirely simulated, so great is the power of suggestion, or, more accurately, of previous conditioning. This lends support to the theory that the pains of normal childbirth are for the most part the psychological consequence of a basic cultural position: in the simplest terms, a woman suffers when giving birth because, from time immemorial, she has been told that she was bound to do so.

No one pretends that childbirth is absolutely painless; even animals, after all, show certain signs of pain in producing their young. But the slight pangs of normal parturition can be tremendously amplified by the effect of an upbringing and tradition which represent those pangs as being inevitable and predestined, and exaggerate their severity through both the spoken and the written word.

The frightened mother contracts her muscles, and this impedes the normal course of delivery; physiological pain is added to psychological; as in so many human processes, the rebound mechanism comes into full operation. The same phenomenon occurs in an ordinary examination of the urethra. Provided the wall of the urethra is not inflamed, the introduction of a probe is completely painless, but every patient feels alarmed merely at the thought of a foreign body being inserted into that part. The sphincter is unconsciously contracted in self-defense, and, according as the doctor proceeds with or without tact and insight, the passing of the probe is painless or painful.

In 1899, a French physician, Paul Joire, of Lille, had become convinced that pain was not an inescapable corollary of parturition, and by administering suggestion in the waking state he was spectacularly successful in obtaining painless childbirth; so much so, indeed, that his patient would tell him, as the head of the infant reached the vulva, that "she could perfectly well feel the opening of the labia, but felt no pain at all."

Many years earlier, hypnosis had been used for achieving painless birth: for example, by Gerling, a German, in 1840, Lafontaine, a Swiss, in 1863, the Frenchmen Charcot (at the Salpêtrière) and Bernheim (of Nancy), and the Russian doctor Dobrovolskaya, about 1880, and others. The disadvantage of the hypnotic method is not only that it sometimes leads to psychological complications, but also that it demands the presence of an experienced hypnotist. It is, moreover, an isolated therapeutic technique which runs counter to the main preoccupation, the education of the expectant mother; to employ hypnosis amounts to declaring in advance that childbirth is painful, since steps are being taken to suppress pain.

The Soviet school, on the other hand, concentrates above all on removing the mother's fear. Dr. Lamaze writes: "Instead of hypnosis and suggestion, which content themselves simply with treating pain, Velvovsky recommends preventative training, carried out in the waking state, by educational methods. . . . His great objective is to remodel women's ideas about labor pains, to suppress completely the mass psychology which regards such pains as decreed by fate, and to set up instead the idea that there is no need to suffer."

Platonov affirms that "pain in childbearing will disappear as a social phenomenon through the efforts of doctors, but also and above all by the action of society, through the efforts of teachers and writers." The Soviet school never declares that there is no such thing as pain in childbirth but strives instead to set up a conditioned reflex which negatives pain, inhibiting the conditioned reflex established by ignorant people who frighten the parturient mother by telling her that her pains are not only unavoidable, but necessary.

The Pavlovians go much further than the English physician Grantley Dick Read, of Birmingham, who contents himself with the simpler and doubtless more objective affirmation that the emotional state of the woman in labor considerably aggravates her pains. His method of "childbirth without fear" is certainly a notable step forward, but it is surpassed by the psychoprophylactic method, in which the woman is not merely reassured, but invited to participate actively in the labor process, the nature of which is explained to her. The future mother knows in advance the mechanism of uterine contraction, a straightforward physiological phenomenon which does not in itself cause pain, and which in its first stage allows the cervix uteri to dilate, and the fetus to be expelled in the second stage.

The mother is also taught that she is not a mere thing, a passive object being subjected to some extraordinary process, but that she has it in her power to help in the accomplishment of a biological action whose mechanism has been made clear to her. Thus the parturient mother is trained to breathe with a special rhythm during labor; by this very means uterine contraction becomes a new conditional connection (contraction-respiration) instead of being a painful conditional stimulus.

This shallow, accelerated breathing is, moreover, undoubtedly a help because of the extra oxygen it provides just when the system has a big effort to make. From the anatomical point of view, it causes a favorable adjustment in the relationship of uterus to diaphragm; its analgesic effect, however, depends on the new conditional connection.

Another feature is training in the "directed push" at the moment of expulsion. All the features of the technique unite to form a physiological and psychological harmony which will transform the parturient mother of the future from a groaning invalid, which is what she has usually been hitherto, into an active participant in the most impressive action in the whole of life—an action to be successfully performed by her, not carried out passively and against her own mistaken resistance.

5

Pavlov's Last Years

Nearing the end of my book and rereading what I have written, I see how many gaps I have left. Some details of Pavlov's experiments have been omitted in the interests of brevity. At the same time, I have perhaps insisted too much on Pavlov's work as a scientist and said too little of his life as a man. But his life was so closely bound up with his presence in the laboratory (whose doors he entered at eight every morning, never leaving till late in the evening, sometimes after midnight) that the man and the scientist merged into one.

Nevertheless, he had the wisdom entirely to abandon his absorbing work once a year. He forced himself to take holidays, during which, his wife relates, he played *gorodki*, gardened and went swimming, and read nothing but literary works, "for no scientific treatise had a passport to accompany us to the country."

Pavlov was a brilliant teacher and had the gift of holding his audience enthralled. He gesticulated as he spoke, had a sense of humor, and provoked argument. It is true that those who ventured to argue with him did so at their own risk, for he was lively and passionate by nature and gave no quarter to anyone who argued merely for the sake of arguing and whose criticism was not constructive. He was capable, indeed, of mordant attacks, and never failed to launch them against

"idealists," even if they were eminent foreign colleagues.
However, he was not afraid to admit it when he had been wrong, and he would often apologize for his intemperate speech to some student who had failed to follow his reasoning with sufficient agility. And though he was deeply aware of the innumerable difficulties, both internal and external, with which the Soviet Government had to contend, and though he rendered homage to that Government for its struggle to abolish man's exploitation by man, he had no inclination to flatter the holders of power, and made no secret of the fact that some of the restrictions imposed by the State were far from receiving his approval. He was quite capable of dealing bluntly with over-zealous officials, and always protected his fellow workers from their interference.

Opinion is unanimous: he was kind, just and honorable. He was completely disinterested, never claiming any advantage for himself or his family. He regarded his life as having been very happy and successful. "I have received," he wrote in his autobiography, "all that can be demanded of life: the complete realization of the principles with which I began life. I dreamed of finding happiness in intellectual work, in science—and I found it. I wanted to have a kind person as a companion in life and I found this companion in my wife, Sara Vasilievna, *née* Karchevskaya, who patiently endured all the hardships of our existence before my professorship, always encouraged my scientific aspirations and devoted herself to our family just as I devoted myself to the laboratory. I have renounced practicality in life with its cunning and not always irreproachable ways, and I see no reason for regretting this; on the contrary, precisely in this I find now certain consolation.

"Above all I am forever grateful to my father and mother; they taught me to live a simple, unassuming life and made it possible for me to get a higher education."

Like all great spirits, Pavlov was a pacifist: "War," he said, "is essentially a bestial method of settling life's difficulties, a method unworthy of the human mind with its immeasurable resources." The idea of an Almighty was repugnant to him. A few months before his death he joined a society of British scientists who proposed "to combat religion," but in accepting membership he made a reservation: ". . . On condition that this struggle is waged solely in the interests of the propagation of knowledge." He would have tolerated no other motive; he had too high a regard for individual liberty.

Grey Walter has reproached Pavlov for not having shown any interest in Hans Berger's pioneer work in electroencephalography. This free, objective criticism lends weight to his other remarks on the man and his work: "Pavlov," he writes, "was before his time. . . . Learning by association is no novelty—the notion is as old as thought—but the ways in which it happens were misunderstood and misinterpreted until Pavlov undertook to measure them. Pavlov has been neglected, travestied, reviled and deified, but the value of his observation and ideas is undiminished, provided his work—or, rather, the many works of his school—be considered as a whole in the terms of the original context. Pavlov himself was, within certain limits of his period, insatiably curious, wide-eyed, broad-minded. In his own words, he was passionately devoted to the study of learning as a measurable phenomenon and, perhaps most important of all alert to the possibility of the unexpected."

Pierre Rentchnick, who has written one of the few—and short—biographies of Pavlov in French, and who is by no means indulgent toward some aspects of Pavlovianism, writes that at the time of his death Pavlov was "venerated by a large number of scientists in different parts of the world."

Pavlov died of congestion of the lungs on February 27, 1936, at the age of eighty-seven. By way of epitaph, let us borrow a passage from the speech delivered by Henri Roger, Dean of the Faculty of Medicine in the University of Paris, when conferring the title of doctor *honoris causa* on Pavlov, in 1925: "The name of Pavlov will live in the memory of mankind. It will remain indelibly engraved after the names of the great physiologists of the nineteenth century—such names as Magendie, Flourens and Claude Bernard."

May 1, 1962

Selected Writings

(*a*) NOBEL SPEECH, DELIVERED IN STOCKHOLM IN 1904

IN the course of our study of the gastric glands we became convinced that appetite acts not only as a general stimulus to the glands, but that it also stimulates them in *varying degree,* depending on the object on which it is directed. For the salivary glands the rule obtains that all the variations of their activity observed in physiological experiments are exactly duplicated in the experiments with psychical stimulation, i.e. in those experiments in which the given object is not brought into direct contact with the mucous membrane of the mouth, but attracts the animal's attention from a distance. For example, the sight of dry bread evokes a stronger secretion of saliva than the sight of meat, although the meat, judging by the animal's movements, may excite a much livelier interest.

On teasing the dog with meat or any other edible substance, a highly concentrated saliva flows from the submaxillar glands; on the contrary, the sight of disagreeable substances produces the secretion of a very fluid saliva from the same glands. In a word, the experiments with psychical stimulation prove to be exact, but miniature, models of the experiments with physiological stimulations by the same substances.

Thus, with regard to the work of the salivary glands, psychology occupies a place close to that of physiology. More than that! At first sight the psychical aspect of this activity of the salivary glands appears even more incontrovertible than the physiological. When any object that attracts the attention of the dog from a distance produces salivary secretion, one has all the grounds for assuming that this is a psychical and not a physiological phenomenon. When, however, saliva begins to flow after the dog has eaten something or substances have been forcibly introduced into its mouth, it is still necessary to prove the presence in this phenomenon of a certain physiological cause, to demonstrate that it is not of a purely psychical character, but is reinforced because of the special conditions accompanying it. These concepts correspond all the more to reality, since, after the severance of all the sensory nerves of the tongue, most substances entering the mouth in the process of eating or forceful feeding evoke, strange as it may seem, the identical pre-operative action of the salivary glands. It is necessary to go further and resort to more radical measures, such as poisoning the animal or destroying the higher parts of the central nervous system, in order to become convinced that between substances stimulating the oral cavity and the salivary glands there is not only a psychical, but also a physiological connection.

Thus we have two series of obviously different phenomena. But how is the physiologist to regard the psychical phenomena? It is impossible to disregard them because they are closely bound up with the purely physiological phenomena in the work of the digestive glands with which we are preoccupied. And if the physiologist intends to pursue his study of them he finds himself faced with the question: How?

Since we based ourselves on the experience we acquired in the lowest organized representatives of the animal kingdom, and, naturally, desired to remain physiologists instead of becoming psychologists, we preferred to maintain a purely objective attitude also in regard to the psychical phenomena in our experiments with animals. Above all, we tried to discipline our thought and our speech in order completely to ignore the mental state of the animal; we limited our work to thorough observation and exact description of the influence exerted by distant objects on the secretion of the salivary glands. The results corresponded to our expectations—the relations between the external phenomena and the variations in the work of the glands could now be systematized; they proved to be of a regular character since they could be reproduced at will. To our great joy, we saw for ourselves that we had taken the right path in our observations, leading us to success. I shall cite some examples illustrating the results we achieved with the help of these new methods.

If the dog is repeatedly teased with the sight of objects inducing a salivary secretion from a distance, the reaction of the salivary glands becomes weaker and weaker and finally drops to zero. The shorter the intervals between separate stimulations, the quicker the reaction reaches zero, and vice versa. These rules are fully manifested only when the conditions of the experiments remain unchanged. Identity of the conditions, however, may be only of a relative character; it may be confined only to those phenomena of the external world that were previously associated with the act of eating or with the forceful introduction of corresponding substances into the animal's mouth; the change of other phenomena is of no significance. This identity is easily attained by the experimenter so that an experiment in which a stimulus repeatedly applied from a distance gradually loses its effect, can be readily demonstrated even in the course of one lecture. If in a repeated stimulation from a distance a certain substance becomes ineffective, this does not mean that the influence of other substances is thereby eliminated. For example, when milk ceases to stimulate the salivary glands, the action of bread remains strongly effective, and when the bread loses its effect owing to repetition of the experimental stimulation, acid or other substances still produce their full action on the glands. These relations also explain the real meaning of the above-mentioned identity of experimental conditions; every detail of the surrounding objects appears as a new stimulus. If a certain stimulus has lost its influence, it can be restored only after a rest of several hours' duration. However, the lost action can be restored without fail at any time by special means.

If bread repeatedly shown to the dog no longer stimulates its salivary glands, it is only necessary to let the animal eat it and the effect of the bread placed at a distance is fully restored. The same result is obtained when the dog is given some other food. More than that; if a substance producing a salivary secretion—for instance, acid—is introduced into the dog's mouth, even then the original distant effect of bread is restored. Generally speaking, everything that stimulates the salivary glands restores the lost reaction; the greater their activity, the more fully it is restored.

However, the reaction can be inhibited with the same regularity by certain artificial means, if, for example, some extraordinary stimuli act on the eye or ear of the dog, evoking in the latter a strong motor reaction, say, a tremor of the whole body.

Since time is short, I shall limit myself to what I have said and pass to a theoretical consideration of these experiments. Our facts fit in readily with physiological thought. The stimuli which act from a distance may be rightly termed and regarded as reflexes. Careful observation shows that the activity of the salivary glands is always excited by certain external phenomena, that, like the usual physiological salivary reflex, it is caused by external stimuli. But while the latter emanates from the oral cavity, the former comes from the eye, nose, etc. The difference between the two reflexes is that our old physiological reflex is constant and unconditioned, whereas the new reflex is permanently subject to fluctuation, and is, therefore, *conditioned*.

Examining the phenomena more closely, we can see the following essential distinction between the two reflexes: in the unconditioned reflex the properties of the substance act as a stimulus with which the saliva has to deal physiologically—for example, the hardness, dryness, definite chemical properties, etc.; in the conditioned reflex, on the contrary, the properties of the substance which bear no direct relation to the physiological role of the saliva act as stimuli—for example, color, etc. These last properties appear here as *signals* for the first ones. We cannot but notice in their stimulating action a wider and more delicate adaptation of the salivary glands to the phenomena of the external world. Here is an example: We are getting ready to introduce acid into the dog's mouth; in the interest of the integrity of the buccal mucous membrane, it is obviously very desirable that before the acid enters the mouth there should be more saliva; on the one hand, the saliva hinders direct contact of the acid with the mucous membrane and, on the other hand, it immediately dilutes the acid, thus weakening its injurious chemical effect. However, in essence the signals have only a conditioned significance: on the one hand, they are readily subject to change, and on the other, the signalizing object cannot come into contact with the mucous membrane of the mouth.

Consequently, the finer adaptation must consist in the fact

that the properties of the signaling objects now stimulate the salivary glands, and at other times do not.

And that is what really happens. Any phenomenon of the external world can be made a temporary signal of the object which stimulates the salivary glands, provided the stimulation of the mucous membrane of the mouth by the object has been associated one or more times with the action of the given external phenomenon on other receptor areas of the surface of the body. In our laboratory we are trying out many such highly paradoxical combinations; and the experiment is proving successful.

On the other hand, rapidly acting signals can lose their stimulating effect if repeated over a long period without bringing the corresponding object into contact with the mucous membrane of the mouth. If ordinary food is shown to a dog for days and weeks, without giving it to him to eat, then the sight of the food will, finally, cease to produce a salivary secretion.

The mechanism of stimulation of the salivary glands through the signaling properties of the objects, i.e. the mechanism of "conditioned stimulation," can be easily conceived from the physiological point of view as a function of the nervous sytem. As we have just seen, at the basis of each conditioned reflex, i.e. of stimulation through the signaling properties of an object, there is an unconditioned reflex, that is, a stimulation through the essential attributes of the object. Thus, it must be assumed that the point of the central nervous system which is strongly stimulated during the unconditioned reflex, attracts to itself weaker stimuli proceeding from the external world to other points of the central nervous system, i.e. thanks to the unconditioned reflex, there is opened for all other external stimuli a temporary, casual path leading to the central point of this reflex. The conditions influencing the opening and closing of the path, its practicability and desolation, constitute the internal mechanism of the effectiveness or ineffectiveness of the signaling properties of the external objects; they are the physiological basis of the most delicate reactivity of the living substance, of the most delicate adaptation of the animal organism.

It is my firm conviction that physiological research will be successfully and greatly advanced along the lines which I have sketched here.

In point of fact, only one thing in life is of actual interest for us—our psychical experience. But its mechanism has been and still remains wrapped in mystery. All human resources—art, religion, literature, philosophy and historical science—have combined to throw light on this darkness. Man has at his disposal yet another powerful resource—natural science, with its strictly objective methods. This science, as we all know, is making big headway every day. The facts and considerations which I have placed before you are one of the numerous attempts to employ—in studying the mechanism of the highest vital manifestations in the dog, the representative of the animal kingdom which is man's best friend—a *consistent*, purely scientific method of thinking.

(b) INTERACTIONS BETWEEN THE DIFFERENT MEDIA *

As part of nature, each animal organism is a complex and integral system, the internal forces of which, so long as it exists, are equilibrated at every moment with the external forces of the surrounding medium. The more complex the organism, the more delicate, manifold and diverse are the elements of its equilibration. There are analyzers and mechanisms both of constant and temporary connections which serve this purpose; they establish the most precise relations between the most minute elements of the external world and the most delicate reactions of the animal organism. Thus, life as a whole, from the simplest to the most complex organisms, including man, or course, is a long series of equilibrations with the environment—equilibrations which reach the highest degree of complexity. And the time will come, distant or not, when mathematical analysis based on natural science will express in majestic formulas of equation all these equilibrations, including, in the final analysis, itself.

But in stating all this, I should like to avoid any misunderstanding in relation to myself. I do not deny psychology as the knowledge of the inner world of the human being. Even less am I inclined to deny anything which concerns the

* This passage, which brought home to the authorities the desirability of erecting the famous "Tower of Silence," was included in a famous lecture entitled "Natural Science and the Brain," delivered at the plenary session of the Twelfth Congress of Naturalists and Physicians in Moscow on December 28, 1909.

deepest aspirations of the human spirit. Here I now simply uphold and assert the absolute and incontestable right of natural science to operate wherever and whenever it is *able* to display its power. And who knows the limits to this!

The researcher who has resolved to register *all* the influences of the external environment on the animal organism requires exceptional equipment for his investigations. He must have in his hands all the external influences. That is why he needs an absolutely new, hitherto unprecedented type of laboratory, where there are no accidental sounds, no sudden fluctuations of light, no abruptly changing air drafts, etc.; in short, it must be a laboratory with the maximum evenness, where the investigator has at his disposal the drives of generators producing all kinds of energy, and the widest range of corresponding analyzers and measuring instruments. Here, there must be real competition between the modern technique of the physical instruments and the perfection of the animal analyzers. This combination will result in a close alliance between physiology and physics, which, it can be assumed, will greatly benefit physics.

At present, because of existing laboratory conditions, the work in question is often not only restricted, contrary to our will, but almost always entails considerable difficulties for the experimenter. He may have spent weeks preparing for his experiment, and at the very last moment, when he is patiently waiting for positive results, a sudden vibration of the building, a noise from the street, etc., destroys his hopes and delays the desired answer indefinitely.

The right kind of laboratory for this investigation is, in itself, of great scientific importance, and since our country has laid the foundations for this kind of research I would like to see it build the first appropriate laboratory, so that this, as it seems to me, highly important scientific establishment should redound solely to our honor and credit. This, of course, can be achieved with the help of public interest and initiative. In conclusion I must confess that this speech has been prompted and encouraged predominantly and mainly by the hope that public interest will be shown here, in Moscow, in this home of Russian glory.

(c) THE CONDITIONED REFLEX

The conditioned reflex is now used as a separate physiological term to denote a certain nervous phenomenon, the detailed study of which has led to the creation of a new branch in the physiology of animals—the physiology of the higher nervous activity—as the first chapter in the physiology of the higher parts of the central nervous system.

For many years empirical and scientific observations have been accumulated which show that a mechanical lesion or a disease of the brain, and especially of the cerebral hemispheres, causes a disturbance in the higher, most complex behavior of the animal and man, usually referred to as psychical activity.

At present hardly anyone with a medical education would doubt that our neuroses and psychoses are connected with the weakening or disappearance of the normal physiological properties of the brain, or with its greater or lesser destruction. But the following persistent, fundamental questions arise: What is the connection between the brain and the higher activity of the animal and man? With what and how must we begin the study of this activity? It would seem that psychical activity is the result of the physiological activity of a certain mass of the brain and that physiology should investigate it in exactly the same way as the activity of all other parts of the organism is now being successfully investigated. However, this has not been done for a long time. Psychical activity has long (for thousands of years) been the object of study by a special branch of science—psychology. But physiology, strange as it may seem, only recently—in 1870—obtained with the help of its usual method of artificial stimulation the first precise facts relating to a certain (motor) physiological function of the cerebral hemispheres; with the help of its other usual method of partial destruction, it acquired additional facts relating to the establishment of connections between other parts of the cerebral hemispheres and the most important receptors of the organism—the eye, the ear, etc.

This raised hopes among physiologists, as well as psychologists, that close connection would be established between physiology and psychology. On the one hand, the psychologists used to begin textbooks on psychology with a preliminary exposition of the theory of the central nervous system, and especially of the cerebral hemispheres (sense organs). On the other hand, the physiologists, when experimenting with the destruction of various parts of the hemispheres in animals, viewed the results obtained by them psychologically, by analogy with the human internal world (for example, Munk's assertion that the animal "sees," but "does not understand").

However, both camps soon became disappointed. The physiology of the cerebral hemispheres perceptibly stopped at these first experiments and made no further substantial advance. In the meantime, many resolute psychologists again took up the cudgels, saying that psychological research should be fully independent of physiological. At the same time there were other attempts to link the triumphant natural science with psychology through the method of numerical measurement of psychical phenomena.

At one time an attempt was made to create in physiology a special branch of psychophysics on the basis of the fortunate discovery by Weber and Fechner of the law (named after them) which establishes a certain numerical relation between the intensity of an external stimulus and the strength of a sensation. But the new branch failed to go beyond this single law. More successful was the attempt made by Wundt, a physiologist who became a psychologist and philosopher, experimentally to apply the method of numerical measurement to psychical phenomena in the form of the so-called experimental psychology; thus, considerable material has been collected already, and more is being accumulated. Mathematical analysis of the numerical material obtained by experimental psychology is called by some people, as Fechner did, psychophysics. But now even among psychologists and especially psychiatrists, there are many who are bitterly disappointed in the practical application of experimental psychology.

So what is to be done? However, a new method of solving the fundamental question was already on the way. Was it possible to discover an elementary psychical phenomenon which at the same time could be fully and rightly regarded as a purely physiological phenomenon? Was it possible to begin with it, and by a strictly objective study (as generally done in physiology) of the conditions of its emergence, its various complexities and its disappearance, to obtain first of all an objective physiological picture of the entire higher nervous activity in animals, i.e. the normal functioning of the higher part of the brain, instead of the previous experiments involving its artificial irritation and destruction?

Fortunately, such a phenomenon had long been observed

by a number of researchers; many of them paid attention to it and some even began to study it (special mention should be made of Thorndike), but for some reason or other they stopped the study at the very beginning and did not utilize the knowledge of this phenomenon for the purpose of elaborating a fundamental method of systematic physiological study of a higher activity in the animal organism. This was the phenomenon now termed the "conditioned reflex," thorough study of which has fully justified the previously expressed hope.

I shall mention two simple experiments that can be successfully performed by all. We introduce into the mouth of a dog a moderate solution of some acid; the acid produces a usual defensive reaction in the animal: by vigorous movements of the mouth, it ejects the solution, and at the same time an abundant quantity of saliva begins to flow first into the mouth and then overflows, diluting the acid and cleansing the mucous membrane of the oral cavity. Now let us turn to the second experiment. Just prior to introducing the same solution into the dog's mouth, we repeatedly act on the animal by a certain external agent—say, a definite sound. What happens then? It suffices simply to repeat the sound, and the same reaction is fully reproduced—the same movements of the mouth and the same secretion of saliva.

Both of the above-mentioned facts are equally exact and constant. And both must be designated by one and the same physiological term—"reflex." Both disappear if we sever either the motor nerves of the mouth musculature and the secretory nerves of the salivary glands, i.e. the efferent drives, or the afferent drives going from the mucous membrane of the mouth and from the ear, and finally, if we destroy the central exchange where the nervous current (i.e. the moving process of nervous excitation) passes from the afferent to the efferent drives; for the first reflex this is the medulla oblongata, for the second it is the cerebral hemispheres.

In the light of these facts even the strictest judgment cannot raise any objection to such a physiological conclusion; at the same time, however, there is a manifest difference between the two reflexes. In the first place, their centers, as already mentioned, are different. In the second place, as is clear from the procedure of our experiments, the first reflex was reproduced without any preparation or special condition, while the second was obtained by means of a special method.

This means that in the first case there took place a direct passage of the nervous current from one kind of drive to the other, without any special procedure. In the second case the passage demanded a certain preliminary procedure. The next natural assumption is that in the first reflex there was a direct conduction of the nervous current, while in the second it was necessary preliminarily to prepare the way for it; this concept had long been known to physiology and had been termed "Bahnung." Thus, in the central nervous system there are two different central mechanisms—one directly conducting the nervous current and the second closing and opening it.

There is nothing surprising in this conclusion. The nervous system is the most complex and delicate instrument on our planet, by means of which relations, connections are established between the numerous parts of the organism, as well as between the organism, as a highly complex system, and the innumerable, external influences. If the closing and opening of electric current is now regarded as an ordinary technical device, why should there be any objection to the idea that the same principle acts in this wonderful instrument? On this basis the *constant connection between the external agent and the response of the organism, which it evokes, can be rightly called an unconditioned reflex, and the temporary connection—a conditioned reflex.*

The animal organism, as a system, exists in surrounding nature thanks only to the continuous equilibration of this system with the environment, i.e. thanks to definite reactions of the living system to stimulations reaching it from without, which in higher animals is effected mainly by means of the nervous system in the shape of reflexes. This equilibration, and consequently, the integrity both of the individual organism and of its species, is ensured first of all by the simplest unconditioned reflexes (such as coughing when foreign substances enter the larynx), as well as by the most complex ones, which are usually known as instincts—alimentary, defensive, sexual and others. The reflexes are caused both by internal agents arising within the organism and by external agents, and this ensures the perfection of the equilibration. But the equilibrium attained by these reflexes is complete only when there is an absolute constancy of the external environment. But since the latter, being highly varied, is always fluctuating, the unconditioned, or constant connections are not sufficient; they must be supplemented by conditioned reflexes, or temporary connections.

For example, it is not sufficient for the animal to take the food placed before it—in this case it would often be hungry and die of starvation; the animal must discover the food by its various accidental and temporary symptoms, and the latter are precisely conditioned (signaling) stimuli exciting the animal's movement toward the food which ends in its introduction into the mouth, i.e. in general, they evoke a conditioned alimentary reflex. The same holds for everything of importance for the well-being of the organism and the species both in the positive and in the negative senses, i.e. for everything which the animal must take from the environment and against which it must be on guard.

No great power of imagination is needed to realize at once what a truly innumerable quantity of conditioned reflexes are constantly effected by the most complex system of the human being who is placed not only in a very broad natural environment, but often also in a very broad specifically social environment, which, on the overall scale, embraces all mankind. Let us take this alimentary reflex. How many diverse conditioned temporary connections, both generally natural and specifically social, are required by a human being to secure adequate and wholesome food—and all this is, in essence, a conditioned reflex

There is no need to explain this in greater detail.

Let us make a leap and turn directly to the question of the so-called tact in life as a specifically social phenomenon. Tact means the ability to create for oneself a favorable standing in society—the quality infrequently met with, of being able to establish with everyone and in any circumstances relations that constantly evoke a generally favorable attitude; it means changing one's attitude toward other people according to their temper, sentiments and the given conditions, i.e. to react to other people depending on the positive or negative results of the previous intercourse with them. True, there is worthy and unworthy tact, the tact which does not violate self-respect and the dignity of other people, and there is the tact which is quite the reverse; but in their physiological essence both are temporary connections, conditioned reflexes.

Thus, the temporary nervous connection is the most universal physiological phenomenon both in the animal world and in ourselves. At the same time it is a psychological phenomenon—that which the psychologists call association, whether it be combinations derived from all manner of actions or impressions, or combinations derived from letters, words and thoughts.

Are there any grounds for differentiation, for distinguishing between that which the physiologist calls the temporary connection and that which the psychologist terms association? They are fully identical; they merge and absorb each other. Psychologists themselves seem to recognize this, since they (at least some of them) have stated that the experiments with conditioned reflexes provide a solid foundation for associative psychology, i.e. psychology which regards association as the base of psychical activity. This is all the more true, since it is possible to form a new conditioned stimulus with the help of an elaborated conditioned stimulus; and recently it was convincingly proved on a dog that two indifferent stimuli repeated in succession can also become interconnected and provoke each other. The conditioned reflex has become the central phenomenon in physiology; it has made possible a more profound and exact study both of the normal and pathological activity of the cerebral hemispheres. Of course, the results of this study, which so far has yielded an enormous quantity of facts, can be described here only in general outline.

The basic condition for the formation of a conditioned reflex is, generally speaking, a single or repeated coincidence of the indifferent stimulus with the unconditioned one. The formation of the reflex is quickest and meets with least difficulties when the first stimulus directly precedes the second, as shown in the above-mentioned auditory acid reflex.

The conditioned reflex is formed on the basis of all unconditioned reflexes and from various agents of the internal medium and external environment both in their simplest and most complex forms, but with one limitation: it is formed only from those agents for the reception of which there are receptor elements in the cerebral hemispheres. Thus we have before us a very extensive synthesizing activity effected by this part of the brain.

But this is not enough. The conditioned temporary connection is at the same time highly specialized, reaching the heights of complexity and extending to the most minute fragmentation of the conditioned stimuli as well as of some activities of the organism, particularly such as the skeletal movements and the speech movements. Thus we have before us a highly delicate analyzing activity of the same cerebral hemispheres! Hence the enormous breadth and depth of the organism's adaptability, of its equilibration with the surrounding world.

The synthesis is, apparently, a phenomenon of nervous coupling.

Nervous Excitation and Inhibition

What, then, is the analysis as a nervous phenomenon? Here we have several separate physiological factors. The foundation for the analysis is provided first of all by the peripheral endings of all the afferent nervous conductors of the organism, each one of which is specially adjusted to transform a definite kind of energy (both inside and outside the organism) in the process of nervous excitation; this process is then conducted to special, less numerous cells of the lower parts of the central nervous system, as well as to the highly numerous special cells of the cerebral hemispheres. From there, however, the process of nervous excitation usually irradiates to various cells over a greater or lesser area. This explains why when the conditioned reflex has been elaborated, say, to one definite tone, not only all the other tones, but even many of the other sounds produce the same conditioned reaction. In the physiology of the higher nervous activity this is known as the generalization of conditioned reflexes. Consequently, here we simultaneously meet with phenomena of coupling and irradiation. But afterward the irradiation gradually becomes more and more limited; the excitatory process concentrates in the smallest nervous point of the cerebral hemispheres, probably the group of corresponding special cells. This limitation is most rapidly effected by means of another basic nervous process known as inhibition.

This is how the process develops. First we elaborate a conditioned generalized reflex to a definite tone. Then we continue our experiment with this reflex, constantly accompanying and reinforcing it with the unconditioned reflex; but along with it we apply other, so to speak, spontaneously acting tones, but without any reinforcement. The latter gradually lose their effect, and, finally, the same thing takes place with the closest tone; for example, a tone of 500 oscillations per second will produce an effect, whereas the tone of 498 oscillations will not, i.e. it will be differentiated. These tones, which have now lost their effect, are inhibited. This is proved in the following way:

If immediately after the application of the inhibited tone we apply the constantly reinforced conditioned tone, the latter will either produce no effect at all or a considerably lesser effect than usual. This signifies that the inhibition which has eliminated the effect of all accessory tones, has acted on this tone as well. But this is a fleeting phenomenon—it is no longer observed if some time passes after the application of the inhibited tones. From this it can be deduced that the inhibitory process irradiates in the same way as the excitatory process. But the more frequently the non-reinforced tones are repeated, the more concentrated becomes the inhibitory process both in space and in time. Consequently, the analysis begins with the special activity of the peripheral mechanisms of the afferent conductors and is terminated in the cerebral hemispheres by means of the inhibitory process. The case of inhibition described above is known as differential inhibition. I shall mention other cases.

In order to obtain a definite, more or less constant strength of the conditioned effect, usually, after a certain period of action of the conditioned stimulus, the latter is supplemented by an unconditioned stimulus, that is, it is reinforced. Then, depending on the duration of the isolated application of the conditioned stimulus, no effect is observed during the first seconds or minutes of the stimulation, since being premature as a signal of the unconditioned stimulus, it is inhibited. This is the analysis of the different moments of the acting stimulus. Inhibition of this kind is called the inhibition of a delayed reflex. But the conditioned stimulus, as a signaling one, is itself corrected by the inhibition, gradually being reduced to zero, if it is not reinforced during a certain period of time.

This is the extinguishing inhibition. It persists for some time and then disappears of itself. The restoration of the extinguished conditioned effect of the stimulus is accelerated by reinforcement.

Thus, there are positive conditioned stimuli, i.e. provoking an excitatory process in the cerebral cortex, and negative ones, provoking an inhibitory process.

In the above cases we have a special inhibition of the cerebral hemispheres, the cortical inhibition. It arises under certain conditions at points where previously it was absent, it varies in size and disappears under other conditions; this distinguishes it from a more or less constant and stable inhibition of the lower parts of the central nervous system, and this is why, in contrast to the latter (i.e. to external inhibition), it is called "internal inhibition." It would be more correct to call it elaborated, conditioned inhibition.

The participation of inhibition in the work of the cerebral hemispheres is as continuous, complex and delicate as that of the excitatory process.

Just as in some cases the stimulations coming into the hemispheres from without enter into connection with definite cerebral points which are in a state of excitation, in other cases similar stimulations can, also on the basis of simultaneity, enter into temporary connection with the inhibitory state of the cortex, if there is any. This follows from the fact that such stimuli have an inhibitory effect, evoke by themselves an inhibitory process in the cortex and are conditioned negative stimuli. In this case, as in the foregoing cases, we have a conversion, under certain conditions, of the excitatory process into the inhibitory. And this can to a degree be explained if we recall that in the peripheral apparatus of the afferent conductors there takes place a constant transformation of various kinds of energy into an excitatory process. Why, then, should there not take place in certain conditions a similar transformation of the energy of the excitatory process into the energy of the inhibitory process, and vice versa?

As we have just seen, both the excitatory and inhibitory processes, arising in the cerebral hemispheres, first spread over them or irradiate, and then concentrate in the point of origin. This is one of the fundamental laws of the entire central nervous system, but there, in the cerebral hemispheres, it manifests itself with the mobility and complexity which are inherent only in them.

Among the conditions that determine the onset and course of irradiation and concentration of the processes, the strength of these processes must be considered of prime importance. The facts that have been accumulated to date entitle us to draw the conclusion that given a weak excitatory process irradiation takes place, given a medium one—concentration, and under a very strong one—again irradiation.

Exactly the same thing occurs in the inhibitory process.

On Hypnosis

Cases of irradiation accompanying very strong processes are observed more seldom, and, therefore, have been less investigated, especially under inhibition.

The irradiation of a weak excitatory process, being of a temporary character, discloses the latent state of excitation that is caused by another acting stimulus (but too weak to be revealed) or by a stimulus that had acted not long before, and finally by one that was often repeated and resulted in an increased tonus of a certain cortical point. On the other hand, their radiation eliminates the inhibitory state of other points of the cortex. This phenomenon is known as disinhibition: the irradiation of an accessory weak stimulus transforms the effect of a certain acting negative conditioned stimulus into the opposite, positive effect. When the excitatory process is of medium strength, it concentrates in a definite and limited point and is manifested in certain activity. Under very strong excitation, the irradiation evokes the highest tonus of the cortex, and against the background of this excitation all other successive stimulations produce the maximum effect.

The irradiation of a weak inhibitory process is what we call hypnosis; under alimentary conditioned reflexes it manifests itself in both the secretory and motor components. When in the above-mentioned conditions there arises inhibition (differential and others), the development of peculiar states of the cerebral hemisphere is the most common fact. At first, contrary to the rule of a more or less parallel change in the size of the salivary effect of the conditioned alimentary reflexes, corresponding to the physical intensity of the stimuli, all stimuli become equal in effect (the equalization phase). Then the weak stimuli provoke a more abundant secretion of saliva than the strong (the paradoxical phase). And, finally, there takes place a distortion of the effects: the conditioned positive stimulus remains fully ineffective, whereas the negative stimulus produces a secretion of saliva (the ultra-paradoxical phase).

The same thing occurs with the motor reaction: when, for example, food is offered to the dog (i.e. when natural conditioned stimuli begin to act), the dog turns away from it; on the contrary, when the food is being removed, taken away, the dog reaches for it. Besides, in the state of hypnosis, in the case of alimentary conditioned reflexes, it is sometimes possible clearly to observe a gradual irradiation of inhibition over the motor region of the cortex. First the tongue and the masticatory muscles become paralyzed, then the inhibition of the cervical muscles follows, and, finally, of all muscles of the body.

Given a further downward irradiation of the inhibition along the brain, a state of catalepsy is sometimes observed, and finally general sleep sets in. The hypnotic state, being of an inhibitory nature, enters quite easily, on the basis of simultaneity, into temporary conditioned connection with the numerous external agents.

When the inhibitory process is intensified, it becomes concentrated. This leads to delimitation between the cortical point that is in a state of excitation and the points in a state of inhibition. And since there is a multitude of diverse points in the cortex, excitatory and inhibitory, relating both to the external world (visual, auditory and others) and to the internal world (motor, etc.), it represents a grandiose mosaic of intermittent points of various properties and various degrees of strength of the excitatory and inhibitory states. Thus, the alert working state of an animal or of a human being is a mobile and at the same time localized process of fragmentation of the excitatory and inhibitory states of the cortex, now in large, now in very small parts; it contrasts with the state of sleep when inhibition at the height of its intensity and extensity is spread evenly over the whole mass of the cerebral hemispheres, as well as down to a certain level. However, even then there may remain separate excitatory points in the cortex—which are, so to speak, on guard or on duty. Consequently, in the alert state both processes are in permanent mobile equilibrium, as if struggling with each other. If the mass of external or internal stimulations falls off at once, a marked predominance of the inhibitory process takes place over the excitatory. Some dogs, in which the peripheral basic external receptors (visual, auditory and olfactory) are damaged, sleep twenty-three hours a day.

Along with the law of irradiation and concentration of the nervous processes, there is another permanently operating fundamental law—the law of reciprocal induction. According to this law, the effect of the positive conditioned stimulus becomes stronger when it is applied immediately or shortly after the concentrated inhibitory stimulus, just as the effect of the inhibitory stimulus proves to be more exact and profound after the concentrated positive stimulus. The reciprocal induction manifests itself both in the circumference of the point of excitation or inhibition simultaneously with their action, and in the point itself after the termination of the processes.

It is clear that the law of irradiation and concentration and the law of reciprocal induction are closely interconnected, mutually limiting, balancing and reinforcing each other and thereby determining the exact correlation between the activity of the organism and the conditions of the external environment.

Both laws operate in all parts of the central nervous system, but in the cerebral hemispheres they manifest themselves in newly arising points of excitation and inhibition, and in the lower parts of the central nervous system—in more or less permanent points.

In the theory of conditioned reflexes, negative induction, i.e. the emergence or intensification of inhibition in the circumference of a point of excitation, was previously called external inhibition, when the given conditioned reflex diminished and disappeared as a result of the action on the animal of an accessory, accidental stimulus, more often evoking an orienting reflex. It was this that gave the occasion to group all the cases of inhibition described above (extinguishing and others), occurring without the interference of outside stimulation, under the common name of internal inhibition.

Besides these two different cases of inhibition in the cerebral hemispheres, there is a third one. When the conditioned stimuli are physically very strong, the rule of direct proportionality between the strength of the effect produced by these stimuli and their physical intensity is violated; their effect becomes not stronger, but weaker than that of moderate stimuli; this is the so-called transmarginal inhibition. This inhibition arises both under the action of a very strong conditioned stimulus and in the case of summation of separate and not very strong stimuli. It is natural to regard transmarginal inhibition as a kind of reflex inhibition.

If we systematize the cases of inhibition more exactly, we shall have either permanent, unconditioned inhibition (inhibition of negative induction and transmarginal inhibition), or temporary, conditioned inhibition (extinguishing, differential and retarding). However, from the point of view of their physicochemical foundation, there is every reason to regard all these kinds of inhibition as one and the same process, but arising under different conditions.

The entire establishment and distribution in the cortex of excitatory and inhibitory states, taking place in a certain period under the action of external and internal stimuli, becomes more and more fixed under uniform, recurring conditions and is effected with ever-increasing ease and automatism. Thus, there appears a dynamic stereotype (systematization) in the cortex, the maintenance of which becomes an increasingly less difficult nervous task; but the stereotype becomes inert, little susceptible to change and resistant to new conditions and new stimulations. Any initial elaboration of a stereotype is, depending on the complexity of the system of stimuli, a difficult and often an extraordinary task.

On the Question of "Temperament"

The study of conditioned reflexes in numerous dogs gradually led to the idea of different nervous systems in different animals, until, finally, sufficient data were obtained to systematize the nervous systems according to some of their basic properties. There proved to be three such properties: the strength of the basic nervous processes (excitatory and inhibitory), their equilibrium and their mobility.

Actual combinations of these three properties produce four more or less strongly pronounced types of nervous system. According to the strength, the animals are divided into strong and weak types; according to the equilibrium of the nervous processes, the strong animals are divided into equilibrated and unequilibrated; and the equilibrated strong animals are divided into labile and inert.

This, approximately, coincides with the classical systematization of temperaments.

Thus, there are strong but unequilibrated animals in which both nervous processes are strong, the excitatory process, however, predominating over the inhibitory; this is the excitable, impetuous type, or choleric, according to Hippocrates. Further, there are strong, quite equilibrated but inert animals; this is the inert, slothful type, or phlegmatic, according to Hippocrates' classification. Then come the strong, quite equilibrated, but labile animals; this is the lively, active type, or sanguine, according to Hippocrates. And, finally, there is the weak type, which is closest to Hippocrates' melancholic type; the predominant and common feature of this type is quick inhibitability due to internal inhibition that is always weak and easily irradiates, and especially to external inhibition under the action of various, even inconsiderable, accessory external stimuli. In other respects it is less uniform than all other types; it includes various animals: those in which both nervous processes are equally weak; those in which the inhibitory process is predominantly very weak; fussy animals, constantly glancing around, and, on the contrary, animals constantly halting, as if becoming petrified. The cause of this non-uniformity lies, of course, in the fact that animals of the weak type, as well as those of the strong type, differ in other features, apart from the strength of the nervous processes. But the predominant and extreme weakness now of the inhibitory process, now of both processes, abolishes the vital significance of the variations of all other features. Constant and strong inhibitability makes all these animals equally disabled.

Thus, type is a congenital, constitutional form of the nervous activity of the animal—the genotype. But since the animal is exposed from the day of its birth to the most varied influences of the environment, to which it must inevitably respond by definite actions which often become more and more fixed and, finally, established for life, the ultimate nervous activity of the animal (phenotype, character) is an alloy of the characteristics of type and the changes produced by the external environment.

Physiology and Psychology

All that has been said above, obviously, represents indubitable physiological material, i.e. the objectivity reproduced normal physiological activity of the higher part of the central nervous system; and it is precisely with this activity that the study of every part of the animal organism must begin and actually does begin. However, this does not prevent certain physiologists from regarding the above facts as having no relation to physiology—a case of conservatism not infrequent in science!

It is not difficult to bring this physiological activity of the higher part of the animal brain into natural and direct connection with numerous manifestations of our subjective world.

As already mentioned, a conditioned connection is, apparently, what we call association by simultaneity. The generalization of a conditioned connection corresponds to what is called association by likeness. The synthesis and analysis of conditioned reflexes (associations) are, in essence, the same as the basic processes of our mental activity. When we are absorbed in our thoughts or carried away by certain work, we do not see and hear what is going on around us; this is obvious negative induction.

Who would separate in the unconditioned highly complex reflexes (instincts) the physiological, the somatic from the psychical, i.e. from the powerful emotions of hunger, sexual attraction, anger, etc.? Our sense of pleasure, displeasure, composure, difficulty, joy, pain, triumph, despair, etc., is connected now with the conversion of very strong instincts and of their stimuli into corresponding effector acts, now with their inhibition; they are connected with all the variations of an easy or difficult course of development of the nervous processes in the cerebral hemispheres, as is observed in dogs that are able or unable to cope with nervous tasks of varying degrees of difficulty.

Our contrasting emotions are, of course, phenomena of reciprocal induction. The irradiation of excitation makes us speak and act in a manner that would not be admitted by us in a state of calm. Obviously, the wave of excitation transforms the inhibition of certain points into a positive process.

A drastic weakening of the memory for the near past—a normal phenomenon in old age—signifies a senile decrease of the mobility of the excitatory process, its inertness, and so on.

When the developing animal world reached the stage of man, an extremely important addition was made to the mechanisms of the nervous activity. In the animal, reality is signalized almost exclusively by stimulations and by the traces they leave in the cerebral hemispheres, which come directly to the special cells of the visual, auditory or other receptors of the organism. This is what we, too, possess as impressions, sensations and notions of the world around us, both the natural and the social—with the exception of the words heard or seen. This is the first system of signals of reality common to man and animals. But speech constitutes a second signaling system of reality which is peculiarly ours, being the signal of the first signals. On the one hand, numerous speech stimulations have removed us from reality, and we must always remember this in order not to distort our attitude to reality. On the other hand, it is precisely speech that has made us human, a subject on which I need not dwell in detail here. However, it cannot be doubted that the fundamental laws governing the activity of the first signaling system must also govern that of the second, because it, too, is activity of the same nervous tissue.

The most convincing proof that the study of the conditioned reflexes has brought the investigation of the higher part of the brain on to the right trail and that the functions of this part of the brain and the phenomena of our subjective world have finally become united and identical, is provided by the further experiments with conditioned reflexes on animals reproducing pathological states of the human nervous system—neuroses and certain psychotic symptoms; in many cases it is also possible to attain a rational deliberate return to the normal—recovery—i.e. a truly scientific mastery of the subject.

On Experimental Neuroses

Normal nervous activity is a balance of all the above-described processes participating in this activity. Derangement of the balance is a pathological state, a disease; and often there is a certain disequilibrium even in the so-called normal, or to be more precise, in the relative normal. Hence the probability of nervous illness is manifestly connected with the type of nervous system.

Under the influence of difficult experimental conditions, those of our dogs that belong to the extreme—excitable and weak—types are quickly and easily susceptible to nervous disorders.

Of course, even in the strong equilibrated types the equilibrium can be deranged by applying very strong, extraordinary measures. The difficult conditions, which chronically violate the nervous equilibrium, include: overstrain of the excitatory process, overstrain of the inhibitory process and a direct collision of both opposite processes—in other words, overstrain of the mobility of these processes.

We have a dog with a system of conditioned reflexes to stimuli of different physical intensity, positive and negative reflexes that are called forth stereotypically in one and the same order and at the same intervals. We sometimes apply exceptionally strong conditioned stimuli; sometimes we greatly prolong the duration of the inhibitory stimuli; we now elaborate a very delicate differentiation, now increase the quantity of inhibitory stimuli in the system of reflexes; finally, we either make the opposing processes follow each other immediately, or even simultaneously apply opposite conditioned stimuli, or at once change the dynamic stereotype, i.e. convert the established system of conditioned stimuli into an opposite series of stimuli. And we see that in all these cases the above-mentioned extreme types fall with particular ease into chronic pathological states differently manifesting themselves in these types.

In the excitable type the neurosis is expressed in the following way: the inhibitory process, which even in a normal state constantly lags behind the excitatory process in relation to strength, now becomes very weak, almost disappearing; the elaborated, although not absolute, differentiations become fully disinhibited; the extinction assumes an extremely protracted character, the delayed reflex is converted into a short-delayed one, etc. In general, the animal becomes highly unrestrained and nervous during the experiments in the stand: it either behaves violently, or—which is much less frequent—falls into a state of sleep; this had not been observed before.

In the weak type the neurosis is almost exclusively of a depressive character. The conditioned reflex activity becomes highly confused, and more often completely vanishes; in the course of the experiment the animal is in an almost continuous hypnotic state, manifesting its various phases (there are no conditioned reflexes at all, the animal even refuses food).

Experimental neuroses in most cases assume a lingering character lasting for months and even years. Some therapeutic remedies have been successfully tested in protracted neuroses. Bromide has long been applied in the study of the conditioned reflexes when certain experimental animals could not cope with the tasks of inhibition. And it has been of essential help to these animals.

A prolonged and diverse series of experiments with conditioned reflexes on animals proved beyond all doubt that bromide bears no special relation to the excitatory process and does not decrease it, as was generally believed, but influences the inhibitory process, intensifying and tonifying it. It is a powerful remedy, regulating and rehabilitating the disturbed nervous activity, on the indispensable and essential condition, however, that it is exactly dosed according to the types and states of the nervous system. In the case of a strong type and when the state of the dog's nervous system is still strong enough, large doses of bromide are to be administered—from 2 to 5 grams a day; for the weak type the dose must be reduced to centigrams and milligrams.

Such bromization for a period of two or three weeks sometimes proves sufficient to cure a chronic experimental neurosis. Recent experiments have shown even a greater therapeutic effect, especially in very severe cases, of a combination of bromide and caffeine, but again subject to very precise dosage of both substances. Sometimes recovery was also attained in animals, though not so quickly and fully, exclusively by means of a regular prolonged or short rest from laboratory work in general, or by the abolition of the difficult tasks in the system of conditioned reflexes.

The described neuroses in animals can best be compared with neurasthenia in human beings, especially since some neuropathologists insist on two forms of neurasthenia—excitatory and depressive. Besides, certain traumatic neuroses may correspond to them, as well as other reactive pathological states. It may be assumed that recognition of two signaling systems of reality in man will lead specially to an understanding of the mechanisms of two human neuroses—hysteria and psychasthenia. If, on the basis of the predominance of one system over the other, people can be divided into a predominantly thinking type and a predominantly artistic type, then it is clear that in pathological cases of a general disequilibrium of the nervous system, the former will become psychasthenics and the latter hysterics.

Along with elucidation of the mechanisms of neuroses, the physiological study of the higher nervous activity provides a clue to an understanding of certain aspects and phenomena, in the picture of psychoses. We shall dwell first of all on some forms of delusion—namely, on the variation of the persecution delusion, on what Pierre Janet calls "senses of possession," as well as on Kretschmer's "inversion." The patient is persecuted precisely by that which he particularly wants to avoid; he desires to have his own secret thoughts but is certain that they are constantly being disclosed and made known to others; he wishes to be alone, but he is tormented by the persistent sensation that someone else is in the room, although there is nobody there except himself, etc.; according to Janet, these are senses of possession.

Kretschmer refers to two girls, who having entered the period of puberty, and being sexually attracted by certain males, for some reason suppressed this attraction. As a result, they were first seized with an obsessive idea; to their great grief, it seemed to them that their countenance betrayed their sexual excitation and that everybody noticed this; at the same time they greatly valued their chastity. Afterward one of the girls suddenly began to imagine and even to sense that the sexual tempter—the serpent that had seduced Eve in the Garden of Eden—was inside her and was even reaching toward her mouth. The other girl imagined that she was pregnant. It is this latter phenomenon that Kretschmer terms "inversion."

In respect of its mechanism it is obviously identical with the sense of possession. This pathological subjective experience can, without undue strain, be interpreted as a physiological phenomenon of the ultra-paradoxical phase. The idea of sexual inviolability, being a very strong positive stimulus, on the background of the state of inhibition or depression in which both girls found themselves, turned into an equally strong opposite negative idea, reaching the level of sensation; in one girl it was the idea of a sexual tempter existing inside her body; in the other, the idea of pregnancy as a result of sexual intercourse.

Exactly the same thing is experienced by the patient with the sense of possession. The strong positive idea "I am alone" turned, under the same conditions, into a similar negative idea—"There is always someone near me!"

In the course of experiments with conditioned reflexes in various difficult and pathological states of the nervous system, it is often observed that temporary inhibition leads to a temporary improvement in these states; in one dog there was twice observed a patent catatonic state, which resulted in a marked decline of a chronic and persistent nervous disorder, almost in a return to the normal for several days in succession. In general it should be pointed out that in experimental disorders of the nervous system almost always separate phenomena of hypnosis are observed, which gives the right to assume that this is a normal physiological remedy against morbific agents.

Hence, the catatonic form or phase of schizophrenia entirely consisting of hypnotic symptoms, can be regarded as physiological protective inhibition, limiting or fully excluding the work of the disordered brain which, owing to the action of a certain, still unknown, noxious agent, has been threatened by serious disturbances or complete destruction.

Medicine knows very well that the first therapeutic measure, which must be applied in the treatment of almost every illness, is to ensure a state of rest for the diseased organ. That such a concept of the mechanism of catatonia in schizophrenia conforms to reality is convincingly proved by the fact that only this form of schizophrenia shows a considerable rate of recovery, despite the protracted character of the catatonic state, which sometimes persists for years (twenty years). From this point of view any attempt to act on catatonics by means of stimulating methods and remedies is definitely injurious. On the contrary, a very considerable increase in the rate of recovery can be expected when physiological rest (inhibition) is supplemented with deliberate external rest for such patients, when they are kept away from the action of constant and strong stimuli emanating from the surroundings, kept away from other, restless patients.

In the course of the study of conditioned reflexes, along with general disorders of the cortex, there were frequently observed extremely interesting cases of disorders experimentally and functionally produced in very small points of the cortex.

Let us take a dog with a system of various reflexes, and among them conditioned reflexes to different sounds—a tone, a noise, the beat of a metronome, the sound of a bell, etc.; it is possible to induce a disorder only at one of the points of application of these conditioned stimuli, while all other points remain normal. The pathological state of an isolated cortical point is produced by the methods described above as morbific. The disorder manifests itself in different forms and degrees. The mildest change effected at this point is expressed in its chronic hypnotic state: instead of the normal relation between the strength of the effect induced by the stimulation and the physical intensity of the stimulus, the equalization and paradoxical phases develop at this point. Proceeding from the above, this, too, can be interpreted as a physiological preventive measure under a difficult state of a cortical point.

When the pathological state develops further, the stimulus in some cases has no positive effect at all, provoking only inhibition. In other cases the opposite occurs. The positive reflex becomes unusually stable: its extinction proceeds more slowly than that of the normal reflexes; it is less susceptible to successive inhibition by other, inhibitory conditioned stimuli; it often stands out in bold relief for its strength among all other conditioned reflexes, which was not observed prior to the disorder. This signifies that the excitatory process at the given point has become chronically and pathologically inert. The stimulation of the pathological point sometimes remains indifferent to the points of other stimuli, and sometimes it is impossible to touch this point with its stimulus without deranging in one way or another the entire system of reflexes. There are grounds for assuming that in the case of disorder of isolated points, when now the inhibitory, now the excitatory processes predominate at the diseased point, the mechanism of the pathological state consists precisely in the derangement of equilibrium between the opposed processes: there takes place a considerable and predominant decrease, now of one process, now of the other. In the case of pathological inertness of the excitatory process, bromide (which reinforces the inhibitory process) often fully eliminates the inertness.

The following conclusion can hardly be considered fantastic. If stereotype, interation and perseveration, as is perfectly obvious, have their natural origin in the pathological inertness of the excitatory process of the different motor cells, then obsessional neurosis and paranoia must also have the same mechanism. This is simply a matter of other cells or of groups of cells connected with our sensations and notions. Thus, only one series of sensations and notions connected with the diseased cells becomes abnormally stable and resistant to the inhibitory influence of other numerous sensations and notions, which to a greater degree conforms with reality because of the normal state of their cells.

Another phenomenon, frequently observed in the study of pathological conditioned reflexes and having a direct bearing on human neuroses and psychoses, is circularity in the nervous activity. The disturbed nervous activity manifested more or less regular fluctuations. There was observed at first a period of extremely weakened activity (the conditioned reflexes were of a chaotic character, often fully disappeared or declined to the minimum); then, after several weeks or months, as if spontaneously, without any visible reason, there took place a greater or lesser, and even complete, return to the normal, which was again superseded by a period of pathological activity.

Sometimes periods of weakened activity and abnormally increased activity alternated in this circularity. It is impossible not to see in these fluctuations an analogy with cyclothymia and the manic-depressive psychosis. The simplest way would be to ascribe this pathological periodicity to the derangement of normal relations between the excitatory and inhibitory processes, as far as their interaction is concerned.

Since the opposite processes did not limit each other in due time and in the proper measure, but acted independently of each other and excessively, the result of their activity reached its maximum—and only then was one process superseded by the other. Thus, there developed a different—namely, exaggerated—periodicity, lasting a week or a month, instead of the short and very easy periodicity of one day.

Finally, it is impossible not to mention a phenomenon that so far has manifested itself with exceptional force only in one dog. This is the extreme explosiveness of the excitatory process. Certain individual stimuli or all the conditioned stimuli produced an extremely violent and excessive effect (both motor and secretory), which, however, abruptly disappeared during the action of the stimulus—when the alimentary reflex was reinforced, the dog did not take the food. Obviously, this was because of the high pathological lability of the excitatory process, which corresponds to the excitatory weakness of the human patient. In certain conditions a weak form of this phenomenon is often observed in dogs.

All the pathological nervous symptoms described above are all manifested in corresponding conditions in normal dogs, i.e. not subjected to surgical operation, and (especially some of these symptoms, for example, circularity in castrated animals), being, consequently, of an organic pathological nature. Numerous experiments have shown that the most fundamental property of the nervous activity in castrated animals is a considerable and predominant decline of the inhibitory process, which in the strong type, however, is greatly leveled out with the passage of time.

To sum up, we must emphasize once more that when we compare the ultra-paradoxical phase with the sense of possession and with inversion, and the pathological inertness of the excitatory process with obsessional neurosis and paranoia, we see how closely the physiological phenomena and the experiences of the subjective world are interconnected and how they merge.

(This summary of Pavlov's discoveries, written by himself, is the article "The Conditioned Reflex" in the *Great Russian Medical Encyclopedia* of 1934. It will also be found in the *Selected Works*. The subtitles are those inserted by Hilaire Cuny; they are not in the original.)

(*d*) NEUROSES IN HUMAN BEINGS AND ANIMALS

The *Journal of Nervous and Mental Diseases* has published* an article by Dr. P. Schilder entitled "The Somatic Basis of the Neurosis." The author concurs that one "finds all the symptoms of the neuroses" in the disturbed states which my collaborators and myself have also called "neuroses" in experimental animals (dogs) studied according to the method of conditioned reflexes. Such an appreciation, coming from a competent person, is certainly much to be prized by us. But I must object resolutely to the writer's subsequent assertions on the comparative study of neuroses in humans and animals. He says: "The important experiments of Pavlov and his school [on neuroses] cannot be understood except in the light of our own experiments on neuroses. We cannot interpret a neurosis by means of the conditioned reflex, but only by means of the psychical mechanism which we have studied in neurosis."

What is the meaning of these two terms, to "interpret" or "understand" phenomena? They mean breaking down complex phenomena into simpler, more elementary ones. We must therefore do the same in this case as in others: we must interpret or understand human neurosis with the help of animal neuroses, not the other way round.

In man, we have first of all, in every individual case, to define in what way the patient's behavior deviates from normality. Again, normal behavior is very different in different individuals. After that, whether the patient helps or resists us in our inquiry, we must try to discern, through all the disorder of his life, to what conditions, to what gradual process or violent event, we are justified in attributing the origin of the pathological deviation, the neurosis.

* 1932.

Then we must understand why those conditions brought about a certain result in the case of our patient, whereas the same conditions had no effect at all on another individual.

More: why did they involve one man in one pathological complex, and another man in a completly different complex? I am concentrating only on the main point, treating all the relevant questions as if they were one question, leaving more detailed and particular questions on one side. Can fully satisfying answers always be given to all these questions?

But this is only one aspect of the problem, if we are intent on analyzing it completely and profoundly. There is no doubt that the deviant behavior of our patient has affected his nervous apparatus; who, nowadays, would dispute that? Thus the questions, "What changes have appeared in the normal processes of his nervous system, in the given conditions? and how, and why? . . ." demand an answer.

Are not all these demands real? Where are they fulfilled? Have we not our dogs to point out the way?

We see in the first place that neuroses can be induced without difficulty only in an animal which in normal circumstances lacks the necessary equilibrium between the elementary forms of nervous activity, the processes of excitation and inhibition; processes which physiology has not so far been able to decompose. In a given animal, either the process of excitation is markedly predominant over that of inhibition, and the animal cannot sufficiently restrain its activities when the conditions of life demand restraint (the excitable type), or else, on the contrary, the process of excitation is so weak that it is often excessively restrained in relation to the demands of life (the inhibited type).

We have also learned, by exact means, that this equilibrium, which is normally inadequate in our experimental subject, breaks down definitively in certain elementary, clearly determined conditions. Mainly in three conditions, three cases. We use excessively strong stimuli as conditional agents, instead of the weak or average stimuli which determine the animal's normal activity; in other words, we overload its process of excitation. Or we demand from it a too powerful or too protracted inhibition; in other words, we overload its process of inhibition. Or, again, we cause a collision between these two processes: we apply a positive and a negative conditional stimulus, one immediately after the other. In all three cases the animals concerned show a chronic deterioration of higher nervous activity; a neurosis. The excitable type almost entirely loses its capacity for restraint, and becomes extraordinarily excited. The inhibited type refuses food when the conditional stimuli are applied, even though it is hungry. It becomes excessively agitated, yet at the same time remains passive in relation to any change in its environment.

Now imagine that these sick dogs were capable of observing their own experience and telling us what they felt. No doubt they would have nothing to add to whatever we had already conjectured on their behalf. They would all declare they had passed through a distressing, difficult time. Then, those in the first category would say that they had thereafter frequently found themselves unable not to do forbidden things, and they were punished in one way or another for doing them. The others would say that they had become incapable of doing, or could not do without agitation, the various things they needed to do.

What we have induced in these dogs is elementary physiological states; and this, in the present state of our knowledge, is as far as physiological analysis can go. And this is in all probability the ultimate, the most profound, basis of human neurosis, and helps us to interpret or understand human neurosis in the most accurate manner.

Man lives in a complex environment and exerts numerous reactions upon it. In consequence, whether the problem be to analyze or to cure, a human case always sets us a very difficult question: What circumstances proved excessively strong for this nervous system? Where and when did the necessity of acting, and that of inhibiting an action, come into conflict in a way which that system found intolerable?

How, then, in view of the enormous complexity of higher nervous activity in the human being as compared with the dog, can Dr. Schilder maintain that the host of impressions experienced by the neurotic is able to contribute usefully to our understanding of the elementary neurosis of the animal? These impressions are only the innumerable variations of the same physiological processes which appear so clearly in the dog!

Of course, when the physiological analysis of the neuroses and psychoses is carried further, a whole series of questions will have to be answered. Is it possible to induce neuroses in equilibrated nervous systems, or only in disequilibrated? Is the initial disequilibrium of the nervous system of primary manisfestation, that is, an innate property of the nervous fiber itself, or is it secondary, depending on innate peculiarities of the systems of the organism other than the nervous system? Are there not, along with the innate property of the nervous system, other conditions in the organism that determine the normal functioning of that system at different levels?

We are working on some of these questions at the present time, and have already collected a certain amount of material for their solution.

It goes without saying that apart from these particular questions, which bear on the general problem of disturbance in normal nervous activity, another problem also faces the physiologist: that of the physical and chemical mechanism of the most elementary nervous processes, excitation and inhibition, the mechanism governing their relations and the overloads to which they are subject.

(Translated from *Typologie de l'activité nerveuse supérieure* [tr. N. Baumstein], Presses Universitaires de France.)

(*e*) AN OPEN LETTER TO PROFESSOR PIERRE JANET*

Would you deem it interesting to print this letter in your journal and at the same time express your views on the points made by me after careful study of the article published by you last year, "Emotions of the Persecution Delusion"?

I am a physiologist and of late, together with my colleagues, have devoted myself exclusively to study of the physiological and pathological work of the higher part of the central nervous system in higher animals (dogs), which corresponds to our higher nervous activity, usually called psychical activity. You are a neurologist, psychiatrist and psychologist. It seems that we should give proper consideration to our reciprocal work and cooperate in our research, for, after all, we are investi-

* Pierre Janet, *membre de l'Institut,* professor of experimental psychology at the Collège de France, was a highly talented psychologist. He established a large number of psychological laws through the study of pathological data. He was born in 1859 and died in 1947. Janet arranged for the publication of Pavlov's article in the *Journal de psychologie* (nos. 9–10, 1933), under the title, "Feelings of possession [*les sentiments d'emprise*] and the ultra-paradoxical phase."

gating the activity of one and the same organ (concerning which there can hardly be any doubt now).

The third part of your article attempts to interpret the feelings of possession. The basic phenomenon is that the patients objectivize their weaknesses, their imperfections, and attribute them to others. They want to be independent, but they are adamant in believing that other people regard them as slaves who are obliged to execute orders. They want to be respected, but it seems to them that they are being insulted. They want to have their own secrets, but it appears to them that their secrets are constantly being disclosed. Like everybody else, they have their own intimate thoughts, but in their imagination these thoughts are being stolen from them. They have annoying habits or painful fits, but they ascribe them to other people.

You interpret this phenomenon in the following way: Many of the ordinary circumstances of life are very difficult, unbearable and painful for these patients. For instance, the presence at the dinner table of two ladies of the patient's acquaintance, toward whom she had never been ill-disposed before. This constant difficulty and the natural frequent failures fill the patients with anxiety and fear, and inspire in them the desire to get away from it all. Like children or savages, they attribute all their troubles to the malignant actions of others, and this signifies deliberate objectification. Further, you devote attention to the following detail: in all the cases cited by you, we have to do, in your terminology, with binary social acts: to be master or slave, give or steal, strive for solitude or seek company, etc. These contrasts are confused by the patients when they are in a state of depression, the disagreeable opposite usually bearing an objective character and relating to other people. For example, the patient passionately wants to be alone, locked up in her room, and actually she remains alone, but she is tortured by the thought that some malevolent person has contrived to get into the room and watch her.

One cannot but agree with all the foregoing, which represents an extremely interesting psychological analysis. But I take the liberty of disagreeing with you on the interpretation of the last point. You repeat more than once that, contrary to the general belief, these contrasts are not so easily distinguishable. You say: "*To tell and to be told* form a single whole and the one is not easily distinguished from the other, as is usually believed." And further: "*The act of insulting and the act of being insulted* are united by the general concept of insult; but the disorder shows that they may be confused, that one may be mistaken for the other." You explain this confusion by a rather complex combination of feelings.

Availing myself of the facts established and systematized by you, I have resolved to take another way and to interpret them physiologically.

Our general notion (category) of contraposition is one of the fundamental and indispensable general notions, which, along with all others, facilitates and controls normal thinking and even makes it possible. Our attitude toward the surrounding world, social environment included, as well as toward ourselves, would be distorted to a very great degree if there were constant confusion of opposites: I and not I; mine and yours; I am simultaneously alone and in company; I offend and I am offended, etc. Consequently, there must be a profound reason for the disappearance or weakening of this general notion, and, in my opinion, this reason can and must be sought in the fundamental laws of nervous activity. I think that in present-day physiology there are definite indications to this effect.

In the course of our study of the higher nervous activity by the method of conditioned reflexes we observed and investigated in our experimental animals the following precise facts. In different states of depression and inhibition (more often in various hypnotic states), the equalization, paradoxical and ultra-paradoxical phases are manifest. This signifies that the cortical nervous cells, instead of normally producing (within certain limits) effects proportional to the intensity of the stimulating agents, in states of various inhibition, begin to produce effects either of equal strength, or inversely proportional to the intensity of the stimulus, and even of an entirely opposite character; this means that the inhibitory stimuli produce a positive effect, and the positive stimuli a negative effect. I make so bold as to suppose that it is precisely this ultra-paradoxical phase which causes the weakening of the notion of contraposition in our patients.

All the conditions necessary for the development of an ultra-paradoxical state in the cortical cells of our patients are in evidence and have been clearly established by you. When these patients, being of weak constitution, come up against a multitude of life situations, they easily fall into a state of depression, anxiety and fear; they can, however, still desire or not desire something, they have their emotionally reinforced and possibly concentrated ideas of what is desirable or undesirable (I am the master, not the slave; I want to be alone and not in company; I want to have secrets, etc.). And in such conditions this is sufficient to evoke in a fatal way an opposite idea (I am a slave; there is always somebody near me; all my secrets are being disclosed, etc.).

The physiological explanation of this phenomenon would be as follows. Let us suppose that a definite frequency of the metronome acts as a conditioned alimentary positive stimulus, since its application is accompanied by feeding and, because of this, evokes an alimentary reaction. Another frequency of the metronome acts as a negative stimulus, since it is not reinforced by feeding and produces, therefore, a negative reaction: the animal turns away when it is applied. The frequencies of the metronome beats constitute a physiological pair, the components of which, being opposites, are associated and at the same time reciprocally induced, i.e. one frequency stimulates and reinforces the action of the other. This is an exact physiological fact. Further, if a positive frequency acts on a cell which for some reason or other is in a weak state (or in a hypnotic state), then this frequency, according to the law of maximum, which is also a strictly established fact, inhibits the cell. This inhibition, in conformity with the law of reciprocal induction, conditions a state of excitation instead of inhibition in the other component of the associated couple. That is why the stimulus related to the latter now provokes excitation, not inhibition.

This is the mechanism of negativism or contralism.

If the food is offered to a dog when it is in a state of inhibition (or hypnosis), i.e. when you induce it to positive activity—to the act of eating—it turns away and rejects the food. But when the food is moved away, i.e. when you give the dog a negative impulse aimed at inhibiting the corresponding activity, at discontinuing the act of eating, the dog, on the contrary, begins to reach for the food.

Evidently this law of reciprocal induction of opposite actions must also be applied to contrary ideas, which, naturally, are connected with definite (verbal) cells and also constitute an associated pair. Due to a state of depression or inhibition (in our experiments any difficulty arising in the higher nervous activity is usually reflected by inhibition), more or less intense stimulation of one idea leads to its inhibition and, by means of the same mechanism, induces the opposite idea.

It is easy to see that this explanation naturally embraces the peculiar symptom of the schizophrenics—ambivalency—which arises under a highly extended and profound ultra-paradoxical state.

Many people, even scientifically minded people, are moved almost to the point of anger by the attempts to give a physiological interpretation of psychical phenomena; they retort that such explanations are "mechanical," since they want to stress as strongly as they can the obvious inaptitude and absurdity of trying to link subjective feelings and mechanics. In my view, this is an obvious misunderstanding.

At present, of course, there can be no talk of representing our psychical phenomena *mechanically, in the full sense of the word*. We are also far from being able to do this with regard to all physiological manifestations; the same thing applies, although in lesser degree, to chemical phenomena, and it applies fully to physical phenomena. A truly mechanical interpretation is still the goal of natural-science research; the study of reality as a whole, including ourselves, is advancing very slowly toward this goal, and much time will be required before it is reached. Modern natural science as a whole is but a series of many *stages of approximation* to this mechanical interpretation, stages linked throughout by the supreme principle of causality or determinism, according to which there is no action without cause.

And if possibilities are now opening up for explaining the so-called psychical phenomena physiologically, they can be regarded as a certain, slight, very slight, degree of approximation toward a mechanical interpretation. It seems to me that in many cases these possibilities are opening up.

Being now at the psychological stage of your research, you are interpreting the feelings of possession, establishing the conditions under which they arise, reducing them to their elementary components and, in this way, elucidating their general structure, i.e. you are also dealing with their mechanics, with their general structure, but in your own way. I, in the physiological stage of my research, am trying to bring our common problem a bit nearer to true general mechanics, interpreting your fact concerning confusion of opposite ideas, as the specific interaction of elementary physiological phenomena—nervous excitation and inhibition. In their turn chemistry, and, finally, physics, will further disclose these phenomena and their mechanism, thus steadily approaching the solution of our problem.

(*f*) SOME REFLECTIONS AND OBITER DICTA OF PAVLOV

War is essentially a bestial method of settling life's difficulties, a method unworthy of the human mind with its immeasurable resources.

* * *

I dreamed of finding happiness in intellectual work, in science—and I found it.

* * *

In order to make use of the treasures of nature and to enjoy them, one must be well, strong and intelligent. Physiology will teach us better and better, and in an ever more perfect manner, the right way, at once useful and pleasant, to work, to rest, and so on. Nor is that all: it will teach us how we ought to think, feel and desire.

* * *

Remember, science requires your whole life. And even if you had two lives they would not be enough. Science demands of man the utmost effort and supreme passion. Be passionate in your work and in your quests.

* * *

The domain of pathological phenomena is an infinite series of all kinds of specific—i.e. such as do not occur in the normal course of life—combinations of physiological phenomena. This, undoubtedly, is something like a series of physiological experiments carried out by nature and life; frequently it is a combination of phenomena of a kind that would not have entered the minds of modern physiologists for a long time to come and which sometimes could not even be reproduced deliberately by the technical means of modern physiology. Hence, clinical cases will always be a rich source of new and unexpected physiological facts. It is, therefore, natural for the physiologist to desire a closer union between physiology and medicine.

* * *

The method of observation is sufficient only for the study of the simpler phenomena. The more complex the phenomenon (and what can be more complex than life?), the greater the need for experiment. Experiment alone crowns the efforts of medicine, experiment limited only by the natural range of the powers of the human mind. Observation discloses in the animal organism numerous phenomena existing side by side and inter-connected now profoundly, now indirectly, or accidentally. Confronted with a multitude of different assumptions the mind must *guess* the real nature of this connection. Experiment, as it were, takes the phenomena in hand, sets in motion now one of them, now another, and thus, by means of artificial, simplified combinations, discovers the actual connection between the phenomena. To put it in another way, observation collects that which nature has to offer, whereas experiment takes from her that which it desires. And the power of biological experimentation is truly colossal.

* * *

The mechanic completes his apprenticeship by passing a test that consists of assembling the mixed-up parts of the dismantled machine. This should hold for the physiologist too. Only he who is able to restore the disordered course of life to normal can say that he has acquired real knowledge of life.

* * *

There are still in the world large numbers of uneducated, ignorant people, who know very little of the phenomena of nature and the manifestations of social life, because they are deprived of the powerful moral support of education. Religion and the belief in God play, in some measure, the role of a moral support in their lives. If we wish to deprive them of that support, another must take its place: education. Then religion, as a support, will disappear of its own accord.

* * *

I condemn myopic materialism which, in a gross, premature fashion, simplifies the object and debases it in the eyes of lucid, richly endowed individuals.

* * *

All my life I have loved and still love work, mental and physical, and the latter perhaps even more than the former. And I experienced the greatest satisfaction every time I succeeded in transplanting a good idea into my physical work—that is, when I was able to combine brain and hand.

* * *

Words and illusions vanish; facts remain.

* * *

Never funk the hard jobs in science. Study, compare, accumulate facts.

No matter how perfect a bird's wing may be, it could never make the bird airborne without the support of the air. Facts are the air of the scientist. Without them you will never be able to take off, without them your "theories" will be barren.

* * *

If your head is empty of ideas, you will see no facts.

* * *

True scientific theory ought not only to account for all the existing elements, it should also throw open boundless possibilities for further development and, we might say, for endless experimentation.

* * *

When studying, experimenting and observing, do your best to get beneath the skin of the facts. Do not become hoarders of the facts. Try to penetrate into the secrets of their origin. Search persistently for the laws governing them.

* * *

It is often said, and rightly, that science progresses by stages which correspond to successes gained in the field of methodology. Every advance in method takes us a step further toward a wider horizon and reveals objects that were previously invisible. That is why we have to start by working out methods of research.

* * *

The trouble is that in each of us there is still rooted the dualism which regards soul and body as being in some way separate from one another; of course, such a separation is unthinkable from the biological point of view.

* * *

Never think you know everything. No matter in what high esteem you are held, always have the courage to say to yourself: "I am ignorant."

* * *

Do not let pride take possession of you. It will result in your being obstinate when you should be conciliatory. It will lead you to reject useful advice and friendly help. It will deprive you of the ability to be objective.

Glossary

ACETYLCHOLINE: A substance liberated at the terminations of certain nervous fibers by the nervous impulse itself, allowing the impulse to be transmitted and to traverse the synapses.

AFFECTIVITY: The innate capacity for feeling emotions, a capacity manifested by organic reactions of which the motor center is the hypothalamus. Its effects are also registered in the cortex, which enables us to become *conscious* of them. Three main types of such effects can be distinguished: two extremes (pleasant and unpleasant) and one neutral (attention, interest, surprise).

ANALYSIS: In connection with higher nervous activity, "analysis" denotes that function of the nervous system by means of which the variations in the surrounding medium (environment) are broken down so that the organism can attain to a state of more delicate adaptation to that medium. Analysis is inseparable from SYNTHESIS (see below).

CHEMICAL TRANSMITTERS: Substances liberated by the nervous impulse itself, and transmitting its effects to the element innervated. One such chemical mediator of nervous activity is acetylcholine; another is adrenalin, which is secreted by the suprarenal glands and produces effects associated with those of the sympathetic nervous system.

DYNAMIC: A phenomenon is dynamic if it cannot be described save in terms of both space and time (three dimensions of space and one of time). Cf. STATIC.

EEG (ELECTROENCEPHALOGRAPHY): The waves recorded by EEG represent the periodic electrical activity of the brain. They are classifiable in terms of their amplitude and frequency. In normal health, a state of sensory and intellectual repose is characterized by the *alpha* waves [8 to 13 cycles per second], which are prominent mainly in the occipital region, and the *beta* waves, which are of lower amplitude and higher frequency [14 to 30 c/s] and appear mainly in the parieto-frontal zones. The low-frequency *delta* waves [0.5 to 3.5 c/s] are typical of sleep (and of some cerebral pathology).* The *theta* waves, whose frequency is somewhat higher [4 to 7 c/s], are associated with emotivity and anger. [The frequencies given here are taken from Grey Walter, *The Living Brain*, p. 53.—*Tr.*]

ENCEPHALON: The entire group of higher nervous structures contained by the cranium (including, therefore, the cortex), from the medulla oblongata upward. The encephalon and the spinal cord together constitute the neuraxis.

ENDOCRINE: The endocrine glands are those which secrete hormones into the bloodstream. Exocrine glands, on the other hand, secrete either externally (as do the sebaceous glands, for example, which produce sebum) or else into a body cavity (as do the digestive glands).

ENVIRONMENT: This is threefold. There is the *internal environment*, inhabited by the cells constituting the organism. And there is the *external environment*, inhabited by the organism itself; this may be aerobic (air or water) or anaerobic.† And finally there is the *cosmic environment*. These environments are differentiated from one another only very arbitrarily, for convenience of

* See Grey Walter, *The Living Brain*, pp. 32, 170, 184. (*Tr.*)

† Some micro-organisms, known as aerobia, can live only in the presence of oxygen; others (anaerobia) live without it. (*Tr.*)

study; in reality the interplay of forces is such that the environments continuously interact with each other. [In this book, as in the *Selected Works* of Pavlov, the word "medium" is sometimes used for "environment."—*Tr*.]

EVOKED POTENTIALS: Our knowledge of these has been gained from electrocorticography. They are the nervous impulses recorded at neuronic level, and especially cortical level, in response to an excitation somewhere else in the body. They enable us to make a study of localization at first hand, and also of the way in which the various somatic structures are anatomically related to one another.

EXCITABILITY: The property possessed by living matter of reacting to various stimuli, internal or external. This property depends on an *electrical discharge* which does not take place at all unless a certain threshold is reached (the law of "all or nothing" in nervous activity). Excitability varies with the state of the cell.

EXCITATION: A process which brings about a state of heightened activity in the cell and which, in the case of neurons, is also called *stimulation*. The *signal stimulus* initiates reflex action.

HORMONES: Chemical compounds which produce specific physiological reactions, and which are manufactured and secreted by the endocrine glands, one hormonal secretion being in some cases touched off by another. Broadly speaking, the hormones regulate cellular functioning including the functioning of the neurons, some of which (as in the hypothalamus) are reciprocal interaction. It is only this interdependent, integrated functioning that renders possible the organism's activities, both psychological and physiological; and these again are closely interdependent.

METABOLISM: The whole cycle of internal chemical activities necessary for the maintenance of life. It is partly destructive, involving the breaking-down of molecular and cellular groupings, with consequent liberation of energy;

and partly constructive and reparative, building up new molecular and cellular structures. It produces heat and electricity. It is subject to the influence of various regulating factors, notably that of the hormones.

MUSCULAR TONUS: The variable degree of tension in the muscles which is brought about through automatic regulation carried out by the nervous system, resulting in a permanent state of slight tension throughout the musculature, even in repose.

PAIN: Specific behavior and reactions in response to certain excitations which appear harmful to the organism. Pain reactions depend on the unconscious, and are automatic; the center in which they are received is the hypothalamus, from which they are transmitted to the cortex; it is the cortex that translates them into *sensations*. (Since the cortex has no specific pain receptor-centers it will be understood that the cortex itself is insensitive to pain.)

POINT: In Pavlovian terminology, a point is a small zone of the cortex corresponding to a given stimulus. A point is not a neuron, but a group of neurons forming a functional system.

PYRAMIDAL: The adjective employed to denote the psychomotor neurons in the brain, whose axons communicate directly with peripheral motor centers; the word refers to the typical pyramidal form of the cell body. Extrapyramidal neurons are the other cerebral motor neurons, and those associated with them in the pons and the cerebellum.

SELF-REGULATION: An internal automatism resulting from the fact that every effect produces a reaction back on to its cause (retroaction). Cybernetics (the science of self-regulating processes) shows us that the functioning of all dynamic structures, microcosmic or macrocosmic, must, ultimately, be studied as a whole.

SENSATION: The act of becoming aware of a cerebral schema which reflects a sensory excitation; the latter exists independently of the awareness.

STATIC: A phenomenon is static if it can be described in terms of space alone. Cf. DYNAMIC.

SYNTHESIS: That function of the nervous system that consists of connecting the various activities of the organism, and of its coordinating mechanisms, with variations in the environment. As synthesis cannot be separated from analysis, the term "analytico-synthetic activity of the cortex" is sometimes used.

SYSTEM: Any set of physiological processes whose elements interact dynamically with each other. Pavlovian terminology includes, for example, the term *signal system*: the whole set of nervous activities corresponding to a specific category of signals (first signal system, common to animals and man; second signal system, language, possessed only by man).

Bibliography

ASRATYAN, E. A., *I. P. Pavlov, His Life and Work* (Foreign Languages Publishing House, Moscow, 1953).

BABKIN, BORIS P., *Pavlov: A Biography* (Victor Gollancz, London, 1951).

BUIKOV, K. M., *Problems of Pavlov Physiology. 1. Development of the Ideas of I. P. Pavlov* (Society for Cultural Relations with the U.S.S.R., London, 1951).

DANIELOPOLU, D., *Materialistic Traditions of Medical Sciences in the Roumanian People's Republic and Their Development based on I. P. Pavlov's Doctrine* (Roumanian People's Republic, Bucharest, 1953).

FROLOV, YU. P., *Pavlov and his School, The Theory of Conditioned Reflexes.* Trans. C. P. Dutt. (Kegan Paul and Co., London, 1937).

GRAY, H., *Anatomy* (Longmans, Green and Co., London).

MAIOROV, F. P., *A Reply to American Critics of Pavlov* (Society for Cultural Relations with the U.S.S.R., London, 1953).

PAVLOV, IVAN PETROVICH, *Ivan Pavlov, 1849-1936, Centenary Lectures* (Society for Cultural Relations with the U.S.S.R., London, 1949).

PAVLOV, IVAN PETROVICH, *Academy of Sciences of the U.S.S.R., Academy of Medical Sciences of the U.S.S.R. Scientific Session on the Physiological Teachings of Academician I. P. Pavlov, June 28-July 4, 1950* (Foreign Languages Publishing House, Moscow, 1951).

—— *Conditioned Reflexes. An Investigation of the Physiological Activity of the Cerebral Cortex.* Trans. and Ed. G. V. Anrep. (Humphrey Milford, London, 1927).

—— *Lectures on Conditioned Reflexes.* Trans. W. Horsley Gantt. (Martin Lawrence, London, 1929).

—— *The Work of the Digestive Glands.* Trans. W. H. Thompson. (Charles Griffin and Co., London, 1902).

—— *Experimental Psychology, and Other Essays* (Peter Owen, London, 1958).

—— *Selected Works,* Edited under the Supervision of Kh. S. Koshtoyants (by J. Gibbons). Trans. S. Belsky (Foreign Languages Publishing House, Moscow, 1955).

PLATONOV, KONSTANTIN IVANOVICH, *The Word as a Physiological and Therapeutic Factor. The Theory and Practice of Psychotherapy according to I. P. Pavlov.* Trans. David A. Myshne (Foreign Languages Publishing House, Moscow, 1959).

STARLING, E. H., EVANS, REV. and LOVATT, C. *Principles of Human Physiology* (J. & A. Churchill, London).

VAY, DAVID LE, *Teach Yourself Anatomy* (English Universities Press, London, 1948).

—— *Teach Yourself Physiology* (English Universities Press, London, 1948).

WELLS, HARRY K., *Pavlov and Freud.* Pt. I, *Toward a Scientific Psychology and Psychiatry* (Lawrence and Wishart, London, 1956).

Index